THE
NOBLE
TRADITION

Interviews with the
Medical Profession

DANNY DANZIGER

VIKING

VIKING

Published by the Penguin Group
27 Wrights Lane, London w8 5tz, England
Viking Penguin Inc., 40 West 23rd Street, New York, New York 10010, USA
Penguin Books Australia Ltd, Ringwood, Victoria, Australia
Penguin Books Canada Ltd, 2801 John Street, Markham, Ontario, Canada l3r 1b4
Penguin Books (NZ) Ltd, 182–190 Wairau Road, Auckland 10, New Zealand

Penguin Books Ltd, Registered Offices: Harmondsworth, Middlesex, England

First published 1990

10 9 8 7 6 5 4 3 2 1

Copyright © Danny Danziger, 1990

Printed in Great Britain by Richard Clays Ltd

Filmset in 11 on 13½ pt Garamond

A CIP catalogue record for this book is available from the British Library

ISBN 0-670-81961-1

FOR MY FRIENDS JOSH AND ROB:
DR DIXEY AND DR JENKINS

CONTENTS

INTRODUCTION

As many contributors to this book recognize, the body is perhaps
the only thing any individual can claim to be fully and absolutely
his own. As man is born to die, his health is the most vital and
personal aspect of his existence. Furthermore, attempts to stave
off death and disease, to overcome illness and pain and to secure
better health have been pivotal in society, just as the incidence of
disease and mortality has itself helped shape human history. Like
the individual, society cannot be indifferent to health. Epidemic
disease, for example, destroys both. A generally poor level of
individual health – poor hygiene, malnutrition and greater sus-
ceptibility to infection – can have profound demographic, economic and even psychological repercussions. It is hard to conceive
of the material success of the First World in the last 100 years
without the improvements in public and private health. The
Roman satirist Juvenal's ideal of *mens sana in corpore sano* could
today be rendered as 'healthy, wealthy and wise'. This connection
of ideas has rarely, if ever, been more topical and apparent. The
cult of health is a striking feature of the West in the late twentieth
century, especially in the United States of America and, increasingly, Britain. Interestingly, perhaps significantly, this is not a
prominent theme in the interviews collected here.

The human body is infinitely complex, fragile and, often,
inefficient. Ironically, but inevitably, a book about health dwells
on the unhealthy. As Anthony Clare remarks, 'Medicine is about
defect.' Some of it can be fairly gruesome: physical deformity,
AIDS, cancer, the death of children may convince the reader

that, as the leukaemia specialist puts it, 'Life is a sod.' Malfunction
of the body is what medicine is about; even the research scientists'
investigations into the healthy working of the body are directed
to the cure, prevention or restoration of things that go wrong.
Yet there is another side. Against the gloom of AIDS, cancer,
the casualty and geriatric wards, must be set the new discoveries
that offer more hope for the future; for example, the development
of non-surgical, non-intrusive techniques of diagnosis and treatment described by Professor Allison.

If healthiness implies unhealthiness, no less ironic is the fact
that the healthier a society becomes, the more health care it
requires, with more disease being combated, more physical break-
downs mended and more people living longer. This expansionist
consequence of improved public health was not foreseen by the
founding fathers of the NHS and it is in no small degree due to
this miscalculation that Nye Bevan's vision has been clouded by
financial restraints and administrative uncertainty. Instead of
being able to work together towards further improvements in
treatment and prevention, researchers compete for funding, hospitals for capital investment, and nurses for pay. It may come as
something of a shock to hear from those interviewed how easily
the allocation of limited public resources and private donations
are subject to publicity, glamour and fashion rather than proven
value, cost effectiveness and results. The case of the heavily and
misleadingly hyped programme of test tube babies is one example
of this. Equally chilling is to listen to the cardiologist describing
the intractable crisis of priorities of space: given the finite number
of available beds, how many should be allocated between patients
with AIDS, cancer and heart disease? Such choices add a new
dimension to the already considerable burden of clinical decision-
making.

The ENT specialist remarks: 'In medicine nothing seems
adequate.' In particular the research scientists display this quality
of questing: 'Whenever you find an answer to a problem, it really
just forms the basis for the next one.' Unfortunately, the seem-
ingly inexorable expansion of scientific knowledge and clinical

technique has not been matched by available resources to fund a public system (a problem not unique to Britain, if more acute here than in many other countries). The cynicism, disillusion and frustration this has caused is evident throughout the interviews. None the less, the overwhelming majority – researchers, clinical consultants, GPs, nurses – still admire the principles of the NHS, applaud its ambition and cherish its existence. There are no calls for its abolition, even from those doctors and nurses who work in the private sector. On the other hand, the cry for its improvement is deafening. Perhaps the socialist paediatrician voices a thought implicit in many other contributions even from those not sharing her politics: 'Life is about living, it is not about money. You can't possibly make something like the NHS pay . . . it is not a money-making venture, you haven't got a product at the end of it. Health doesn't generate wealth, it just generates health, which is what life is about.'

'We ought to take pride in the fact that despite our financial and economic anxieties, we are still able to do the most civilized thing in the world – put the welfare of the sick in front of every other consideration' – Aneurin Bevan, House of Commons, 9 February 1948.

'The most civilized thing in the world'. Forty years after the National Health Service was established, its founder's words may appear naïve or optimistic, depending on your point of view. In 1948, most doctors hated the idea of a national health service; most patients welcomed it. Now the majority of both accept the NHS as worthwhile, at least as a safety net and at most as a life line. Yet the provision of medical care remains controversial, raising issues beyond even those of political principle and financial management. Medicine is of crucial and abiding concern because health is central to human experience, individual and collective. We have all had contact with the medical profession, with hospitals or local doctors, if not directly, then through the experiences of parents, children or friends. In Britain today, people tend to be born and die in hospital. We all fall ill and suffer pain, which often causes anxiety, even fear, if not material hardship as well. To help us, we look to medicine and medical practitioners.

If the current debate in Britain is about paying for health care, this book focuses on the people who provide it and their personal and professional circumstances. The interviews look behind the clichés of pinstriped consultants, avuncular GPs, ministering angels or hearty medical students. The practitioners themselves examine the stereotypes of their own professsion and, in the process, reveal their motives, incentives, satisfactions and frustrations. Medicine is an ancient art, now an advanced science; perhaps it has always been, in both a secular and religious sense, regarded by those outside as a mystery. These interviews help lift the veil on what to many remains an arcane and wonderful activity, a ritual of almost divine expertise performed by quasi-priestly officiants equipped with familiar, comforting yet distancing props – white coats, stethoscopes, nurses' uniforms, doctors' bags, the smell of disinfectant and ether. These are the images here demythologized.

Health care is as structurally diverse as are the problems it tackles and the society it serves. The front line can be a hospital casualty ward or a GP's surgery. Treatment may be administered at home or in a variety of hospitals and clinical departments. A medical condition may require surgery or a course of drugs; it might end in complete recovery, partial rehabilitation into society or in a hospice. The 'doctor' may be local and well known or a consultant, a stranger with impressive credentials and obvious authority. The patient may receive full information or practically none. Diagnosis and treatment may be delivered by a clinical doctor, but his work will be based on the product of years of laboratory research by scientists who have little or no direct clinical responsibilities. In these interviews the whole range of this medical activity is represented, from the contrasting problems of emergency and long-term hospital care to routine health provision, for conditions such as flu, sprains or pregnancy, preventative medicine in the community and scientific research. Medicine presents many faces: the researcher, the hospital clinician, the

GP, the nurse, etc. Within each category there are extremes of diversity: the inner-city or Outer Hebridean GP; the casualty consultant and the leukaemia specialist, both hospital clinicians; the revered consultant and the harassed houseman. This diversity is maintained in areas of specialism. The neurosurgeon and the orthopaedic surgeon; the ENT consultant and the gastro-enterologist; experts on cancer, leprosy, heart disease, arthritis, VD and AIDS; the anaesthetist, the nurse (male and female, public and private), the physiotherapist and the radiotherapist; the rural East Anglian GP and the celebrated and successful psychiatrist; the paediatrician and the geriatrician; all have their say. The end of health is death, and the treatment of the dying and the bereaved is not ignored. The path from pure research to the chemist's shop is very long, and passes almost infinitely varied scenery. As Professor Sir David Weatherall observes, as you move from laboratories to wards to outpatient units, 'you're moving from very clear science to extremely dirty science'. Within the medical profession research into DNA or the nervous system of a giant squid are united with the intuitive diagnosis of physically and academically remote GPs dealing with boils, headaches and domestic problems. Medicine is political, for it deals with people in society. It can also be ethically controversial. Is there a right to die, for instance? We hear a vigorous defence of experimentation on live animals and an equally forceful debunking of myths surrounding embryo research and test tube babies. The protean quality of medicine, even though it concerns one physical organism – the human body – is immeasurable.

Those interviewed, however, discuss more than their knowledge and skill. Together their perceptions and experiences provide a frank, pragmatic and largely unsentimental view of medicine as a science and of the health service as the application of science to practical physical and human problems. Beside the impressive knowledge runs the theme of ignorance. Researchers, clinicians and GPs never know enough to make them the gods of diagnosis and therapy the patients often seek, assume or expect. On the other side, patients themselves are, in the view of some contributors, oddly tenacious in not understanding or accepting what is good for them. Beyond the detailed explanation of each condition diagnosed, there also sits the question: why this patient with this illness at this time? The ethical, moral, and, at times, religious dimensions cannot easily be forgotten.

These are very personal statements which combine to present a rich and very human picture, so much so that it is not easy to draw any clear conclusions. Here there are scientists, teachers, healers, social workers, technicians, managers and entrepreneurs, all working under similar labels in the same profession. Variously cited as motives for entering medicine are ambition for professional status; a desire to serve; and an inability to throw off, or an enthusiasm to follow, family tradition. Many, probably most, possess or acquire a marked and necessary self-confidence in their ability to handle responsibility and make decisions influencing the lives of others. There are almost no admissions of professional incompetence or even inadequacy, the refreshingly honest, overworked houseman aside. In some, this confidence can be seen to spill over into arrogance, self-satisfaction and selfishness. Many display signs of the domineering obsessiveness of the workaholic. Not all medical stereotypes are disproved by these interviews. Yet this professional self-confidence, most marked in hospital clinicians, goes hand in hand in all areas with a level of personal commitment, of time, emotion, energy and intellectual resource, probably unmatched by other occupations through the intricate but rigid, often stultifying hierarchy. Above all, from nurse to research scientist, from laboratory bench to consulting room, from frenzied casualty ward to country surgery, from maternity ward to hospice, there emerges an overwhelming sense of interest and excitement in the work being done. Amidst the inevitable anxieties, disappointments, frustrations and sadness, almost universal enthusiasm shines out. Much of what is said may challenge opinion, provoke thought, incite argument, but it is difficult to read these interviews without being impressed at the high level of personal investment in the provision of health care in this country. What are the best means of supporting and developing medical services will be, and should be, a matter of lively and vital debate. What follows may help provide a human perspective as well as ammunition for that discussion.

PROFESSOR DAVID ALLISON
RADIOLOGIST

═══════

THE old x-ray pictures are just so completely different to what we can do today, it's a different order: it's just like in the early days of x-rays, a doctor asking: 'Is an x-ray giving us better pictures than we get by looking at the patient?' If you take a picture of, say, the abdomen with an ordinary x-ray, the x-ray will go through all the soft tissues and just give you a picture of the bones: but if you do a CT* scan of the abdomen, you'll see every organ separately delineated: the liver, the spleen, the kidneys, the stomach, the intestines, the spine – and there's no way in which you could separately look at those in a conventional x-ray.

And I think that in twenty or thirty years time, radiology is going to be the most important subject in medicine because it's the place where virtually every diagnosis is going to be made, excluding those diagnoses which are made on the biochemical level, because the area of molecular biology is also expanding *pare passu*.

I opted to go into radiology at a time when it was less prominent as a medical specialty, particularly in comparison with surgery, than it is now. And it so happened that I went into it at just the right moment, because as I went into radiology, the sheer advance of technology in the way of computerization, television technology, image intensification, all those kind of electronics,

---

*CT is a method of looking at cross-sections of the body using ionizing radiation.

made the imaging of the body safer and quicker than it had ever been before, and it made some things that simply weren't possible before possible. Advances in nuclear medicine with the ability to tell us about the physiology and the pathology of the body, all that was undergoing dramatic advance, combined with advances in the actual materials, the ability to make a catheter that we might insert into a blood vessel, which would enable us, say, to put a tube through a small puncture site in one bit of the body, guide it through the arteries and veins of the body, have it radio-opaque so we could follow it on a television screen and then see what the arteries and veins were like in that part of the body and make a diagnosis – all these advances were going on together, and what they led to was a dramatic increase in the quality and range of diagnoses that we could make. And the general public is now becoming aware of things like nuclear magnetic resonance, CT scanning, isotope scanning and ultrasound, all of which have undergone the most prodigious expansion.

Another reason why radiology is becoming so important is that because of the kind of instruments that we can get into the body, not only do we make diagnoses of what's wrong with patients, we've started treating them, and that's the area of radiology that I've made my major interest, which is called interventional radiology.

In some countries surgeons have felt that radiologists are beginning to take over large areas of their territory, and one humorous definition of interventional radiology is 'that branch of medicine where the radiologist intervenes between the surgeon and his bank account'. But we're beginning to occupy the same role as the surgeons, so that where a clinician once referred to the surgeon, he will now go direct to the radiologist.

Say that a patient came into this hospital today, and he's bleeding from his stomach or something like that. What we would do now is to take the patient into the x-ray department – not into the operating theatre – put a fine tube through a percutaneous puncture into an easily accessible artery, guide that tube under x-ray imaging control to the blood vessel we knew to be bleeding into the body, wherever it was, and we would then actually plug the artery off – and that's all the treatment the patient would basically require. In other words we would do an operation without the patient having an anaesthetic, a scar, and a long in-patient admission.

We might want to block arteries that are feeding tumours, to starve the tumour of blood and make it die. And we can block those off far more safely and more effectively than a surgeon can remove them, and the patient won't require any other form of treatment.

Using image guided surgery we can move gallstones or renal stones without an operation; we can unlock blocked blood vessels so that if a patient has got a blocked coronary artery that's causing angina, or a blocked artery in their leg that means they can't walk, instead of them having a difficult or dangerous surgical operation to bypass those blocks, we can now open them up using special balloon catheters or lasers, or even minute drills that clear them open.

Because of modern imaging, we can take a biopsy from any tissue in the body, lungs, spine, it can even be done in the central nervous system, and forming that kind of biopsy is really quite a major part of modern radiology.

In the old days, if you were suspected of having a tumour, or you had a breast lump and we weren't sure if it was benign or not, it had to be taken out so it could be looked at under a microscope, and in the case of a deep-seated lesion, such as something in your lung, that meant a major operation, having your chest opened, and bit of lung taken out, being in a hospital bed for a week or so, general anaesthesia, the whole thing. Now, if you come to me with a lump on your chest, we could put a fine needle into it, using x-ray imaging control, watch it on the television, and within a few minutes we would get a sample without you having anything more than a minute skin puncture. Again, no anaesthesia, no scar, no operation.

With ultrasound, we use special equipment which sends sound waves through the body, and we get pictures of the reflections which tell us not only the depth at which things lie but their character. That is particularly useful in obstetrics, but is also used in all parts of the body now and is particularly useful for looking at the heart and the arteries.

Particular diseases cause changes in particular body metabolisms. For instance, if a patient comes with a carcinoma of the breast, one of the things we're concerned to know is whether that tumour has spread to the bones. Now, if a tumour gets into a bone, eventually it will cause a change; this would eventually show up on an ordinary conventional x-ray, but by the time you would be able to see it, it would be reasonably well advanced. We now use equipment which will detect what things are doing in the body. So if a woman comes in today, say, feeling a lump in her breast, with an injection in an arm vein, we can see within a few minutes the whole of her skeletal system, and within a few hours we would probably know if she's got the metastasis (areas which have spread from the breast to those bones). So it's enormously improved our diagnostic potential, which of course has an effect on both treatment and on our ability to prognosticate to the patient about how far advanced their disease is, their life expectancy, and all that kind of thing. It's just so exciting!

Well, we know that any radiation is undesirable, and so all our efforts are aimed at reducing the amount of radiation that patients get to a minimum. It's important, however, not to get these things out of proportion, because we receive radiation all the time in nature from various sources. Going in an aeroplane at a height of 37,000 feet will give you a considerable radiation dose, and leaving the windows open in the summer will give you a dose of cosmic radiation, but these are things we don't even think about. As far as we know, the kind of levels of radiation we give in diagnostic imaging are harmful to such a negligible proportion that the benefits of what we find out from giving that radiation far outweigh any of the risks or disadvantages.

DR HOWARD BADERMAN
ACCIDENT AND EMERGENCY
CONSULTANT

━━━━━━
━━━━━━

THERE were difficult relationships with my parents, particularly my father. I can remember saying that I wanted to be a doctor at the age of about six or seven, and he once said, and I've never forgotten it, to the parents of a friend of mine – and those parents told the boy, and the boy told me, and it did me the most enormous harm because I exaggerated it out of all proportion – he said, 'Howard will be a doctor like I will be a ballet dancer.' And I've never ever forgotten that phrase. Because he didn't think I was competent to do it, he poured scorn on me, but at the same time he was telling other people, 'I think he's going to be a brain surgeon.' Never in my wildest dreams did I want to be a brain surgeon! A microbiologist, a psychiatrist, who knows? So he had a very ambivalent thing about it: he was very proud, as Jewish parents would be of a son who wanted to do medicine; at the same time it posed a threat to him, to his business and to the succession. I was the oldest son, and he had a small number of retail shops, and so on and so forth. And there is no doubt that he is very proud of me; I mean, there are times when I'm on the television or whatever, and talking about accidents or emergencies or various aspects of it, and people tell him that they've seen me, or he has seen me, and I know instinctively that he is very proud, but he would rather die than talk to me about it, or ask me about it, or comment on it, or whatever. It's a very interesting if somewhat painful relationship.

As they were quite convinced that I would never make it, so I became absolutely obsessional and determined to be a doctor – more to prove that I could, rather than knowing anything about what it meant. I remember at the age of eleven taking out a subscription at the local W H Smith's for *The Lancet*, not understanding a word that it said, but becoming intrigued by it. And I went to the local pet shop to buy a guinea pig, and I forced myself to kill it to prove that I could dissect it, which I then did, much to everybody's astonishment, including my own, and I remember my sister's three-year-old face at the upstairs bedroom window watching me while I was drowning this guinea pig in a lawnmower box in the garden – and she never really forgave me for that.

I was never very bright at school, I never got higher than eighth in my class, but I was an obsessional worker. I would buy great big sheets of graph paper from drawing shops and make out charts of every microbe under the sun, or I would draw out charts of blood cells and malaria parasites, and then – maybe it was a burgeoning of puberty and sexuality – charts of the human body with all the endocrine glands marked out on it. I knew a great deal about endocrine glands before I knew anything about anything else really.

We had a very nice, very bluff GP who came to see me every now and again, and he never told me what medicine was about, but he encouraged me with a wry smile – I remember it very clearly – which instilled a certain confidence. I reckoned if he thought I could do it, then maybe I could actually, and that had a sort of subtle influence. I remember him once standing in my bedroom when I had pneumonia, at the age of about twelve, saying to me with a chuckle, 'You'll rue the day when you're walking the wards' – that was the expression he used, 'walking the wards'; it had a sort of romantic air about it. And he said it in a way which was without doubt to encourage me, and I knew what he meant.

And then long before I took 'O' levels, I wrote to every medical school in the country asking them to tell me what one needed to get in. Most of them wrote back saying, 'Thank you very much, but it's a bit early actually. Write to us again after you've taken your 'O' levels' – which I dutifully did.

I had heard that at a lot of medical schools, mainly the London medical schools, you had to have a relative who was in medicine or you had to play rugby. I was never any good at sport – I was tall, gangly, a rather frail, sensitive flower – but I took up rugby and regularly got thumped. But I could then put on my CV that I played rugby.

And so it became accepted in the family that I would be a doctor, accepted by everybody except my father, who was very against it and wanted me to go into the business.

It was very difficult to get into medical school, almost impossible. I was turned down right, left and centre. And eventually, having applied to all these medical schools and getting turned down without an interview, I got an interview at Bristol when I was in despair – but literally in despair. And it was one of those magical days where everything went well; you know, people were nice to me on the train, and I remember going into a wash and brush up outside Bristol Temple Meads station to comb my hair and polish my shoes, and there was a lovely lady in the gent's toilet who said: 'You look very smart, dear.' And so it went all the way along the line, and when I walked into that interview, there was a great circle of people sitting around to interview me, very intimidating, but for some reason or other – it must have been the first question went right – I knew I couldn't put a foot wrong, and before I left the room I knew that they were going to offer me a place, and they did.

Meanwhile, unbeknown to me, my mother had a word with a Miss Edwards, the manageress of one of our shops, and Miss Edwards had a family GP whom we didn't know, and this GP was a buddy of the Dean of St Mary's. I had applied to St Mary's but got turned down without an interview: the lists were all closed and so on and so forth. And I didn't know anything about all this, but out of the blue I got a telephone call from that GP to say, 'Would you attend St Mary's for an interview on your own next Saturday morning. The Dean will see you.' I was livid that somebody had pulled strings! Anyway I went to this interview, and the Dean interviewed me and said, 'Do you play rugby?' (St Mary's was the great rugby school; they had three, if not five people in the England fifteen), and I said, 'Yes, I do', and he then said, 'What do you play?' and I said, 'Wing three-quarter', whereupon he said, 'Yes, I think we've got a vacancy for a wing three-quarter this year.' And I got in there too.

I told my parents, 'I'm not going, I will not go. I *will not* go.' I was determined to go to Bristol. But at the eleventh hour, I got in off the reserve list at UCL; a letter came saying, 'We are now able to offer you a place at UCL.' My parents were on holiday at a hotel in Bournemouth, and I had to go down to see them, and we spent a harrowing, sort of Woody Allen-like Jewish weekend arguing. I wanted to go to Bristol because they'd accepted me on my merits – as had UCL – but I wanted to get away from home, and they wanted me to stay in London where they could keep an eye on me.

And they talked me into going to UCL, so I turned down Bristol, much to my shame. And I was bitterly unhappy about that.

In retrospect, from the point of view of my career, I don't think it could have gone better had I gone to Bristol, but in terms of my own personality development, I've no doubt it was the wrong thing to do. It took me another twenty-five years to grow up and get away from home, if not longer.

But once at UCL, the reality was terrific. From the day I set foot there, I've never regretted it. It was everything I might have imagined. And the fact that at the end of the day, we would actually see patients, I knew in my bone marrow, or as Jonathan Miller used to say, in my bowels and my water, that it was the right thing for me.

I really knew I was in the right place because I was seeing patients – I was on the wards. The work, it was like music to my ears, there was hardly any bit of the syllabus that I didn't enjoy and do quite well at; I won medals in medicine and surgery, and so on and so forth. And I think one's very lucky in life if you find you're doing something that you sense you're good at, and I was good at talking to patients, and I was good at working with other doctors and nurses, and although I worked unbelievably hard, I had a super time.

I was the archetypal bachelor. One of my jobs was GP to the nursing staff, so I was very eligible, but people said, 'He'll never get married, he'll never settle down.' And part of the thing was a hang-up over my Jewishness. My parents wanted me to marry a Jewish girl, and I didn't meet any Jewish girls, and I didn't particularly want to either – not that I've got anything against them – but I was surrounded by 1,010 nurses, that was the number on the staff, and I had a succession of girlfriends that I had to hide from my parents.

I did eventually marry a nurse, shortly after I became a consultant. We went out for a long time but I couldn't bring myself to take the plunge – there were too many hang-ups of a major nature in my background – and it was on and off and on and off and I caused her great grief and pain over a number of years until I eventually had to say, 'I've got to grow up, I've got to make a decision.' So I did, and it wasn't easy, such is the pressure of family life from that sort of background.

UCH cooked up the idea that they would experiment with a consultant in charge of the casualty department, and they said, 'If we were to invent this new job, would you consider doing it? We could make you a consultant physician . . .' and I jumped at the chance, and I became the first casualty consultant in the country.

Casualty is on the interface of the hospital and the community, it's the main portal of entry. We're here to receive the hundreds of walking wounded with minor ailments and minor injuries, as well as the more major cases, like the coronaries and the road accidents and the burns and the overdoses and the strokes. More than 10 million patients a year come to the country's casualty departments for a first visit for a particular condition. It sees more patients than all other outpatient clinics put together, so it's an absolutely crucial linchpin in the country's health services.

The hecticness is the sheer volume of work, very large numbers of people, 260 patients a day in this department alone; it never stops. Most of them are relatively minor injuries or illnesses, although for the patient they're not minor, you know; a badly cut hand or a sprained ankle, that is really quite important for that patient. About 10–20 per cent are either actually or potentially very seriously ill.

Casualty is unique in that it's open twenty-four hours a day, 365 days a year, and you never know what's going to come in through the door, and you would be amazed, as indeed would my colleagues, if they knew the sort of things we get up to down here, the sort of problems we deal with. It's fantastic. It's galling. It's frustrating. It's annoying. It's maddening. I think that I'm not going to survive the day, I shall have my final stroke by teatime because there are no beds, or we've had one difficult situation after another. The pressures are tremendous. It's not just pressures of patients, but there are never enough beds, there are delays in the x-ray department, the gynaecologists can't come down to give us a second opinion – and we get the stick for all of these things because we're in the front line.

A casualty department is the shop window for the hospital. There's no doubt about it. If you create a bad impression in casualty, that hospital gets a bad name. If things go well in casualty, and patients are speeded through and treated sensibly and sensitively, then that hospital stock goes up. Because we provide medicine for the community, just as GPs do, what an individual patient feels about doctors or nurses may be very much influenced by the sort of experience they have in my department. So it's an influential department for good or ill, in terms of the patient, in terms of the whole community, and in terms of the hospital.

The pressures are on us to process people quickly; you know, the supermarket check-out system. You make the department work sufficiently smoothly to get through the load with the maximum of speed, but what you often lose is the humanity when you do that. And we are particularly vulnerable to falling into that trap. We're not terribly efficient: people do sit around for hours in the country's A & E departments – including my own sometimes – and delay makes people depressed and frustrated and angry. And in our urge to do something about that, it's very easy to lose the ability or the determination to actually talk to the patients. I mean, it takes you five minutes to listen to somebody's heart or their chest, but it's probably more important to spend slightly longer explaining what you've found and what you think may be the problem, and what you're intending to do. When we get thank-you letters here, which we do, really quite often, the thing that people say is not, 'You saved my life', or, 'You put in a marvellous set of stitches': it's, 'They were so kind to me; the porter was kind and the receptionist was kind and the nurse and the doctors were kind . . .' And what they actually mean is, 'They talked to me', 'They touched me', 'They listened to me', and it is quite easy to lose that.

Everybody asks me, 'Are you there all the time?' Well, I'm there to supervise and to organize, but if the show can't run if I'm not there all the time, then you're not doing the job properly. Nobody runs an x-ray department or a Radiotherapy department where the consultant has got to be there twenty-four hours a day, but he gets called in if there's something that the rest of the team can't handle or because he wants to be called in for that particular situation. And that is true in all specialities, or it ought to be.

What most casualty consultants say is, 'I want to be rung up if such and such happens.' I have a list. The sort of things I insist on being called for are multiple injuries or somebody with really very serious injuries – not because we are going to come in and save life, but because we want to make sure that the right people have been called, that there's no delay, no hassle, and so on.

I'm informed of every stabbing that comes in here, because junior staff on duty at night in hospital won't have seen as many as I have, and they may underestimate them. With stabbings, the size of the entry wound can be tiny, and it can have done the most horrendous damage, it can have gone into the heart or a major blood vessel, and it's very easy to underestimate the potential hazard of such a situation, very easy to say, 'We'll put in a few stitches and you can go home', or if it's not bleeding, the patient may insist on going home or try to, and so on. So they call me – God help them if they don't!

I don't believe anybody should come into a London teaching hospital stuffed to the ceiling with consultants, and if they are in danger of losing their life, not see somebody senior. We are unlikely to change the treatment, because the junior staff here are very good, but they don't have the experience, and so to protect them, as well as the patient, somebody senior needs to know.

One of my special interests is children, because they are a special group of individuals. They need very careful handling – not because they're dying or bleeding, not even because they're in terrible pain, but because they don't know what to expect, and may find it difficult to cope with this potentially frightening and hostile environment. And it's particularly challenging . . . I would almost use the word 'delicious', to be able to get it right with a child in casualty, to actually handle that child, its parents and the whole situation in a way which even if you have caused pain, which you might have to do, at the end of the day the child goes out with a tear-stained smile on its face, and will actually say goodbye to you. Then you know you've more or less got it right.

Well, on an average week I will be rung up about six or seven times in the middle of the night, and I will come in perhaps twice, maybe three times. In a bad week I'll come in sometimes twice in the same night. That's the way I want it. I mean, consultants are still, rightly or wrongly, masters of their own working practices. The fact that I insist on being rung up or coming in is a personal decision, and it probably satisfies some need in me, just as much as it satisfies the need of the patients. I don't think there's any doubt about that.

I remember my father never wanting to come home from his shops; he used to drive us mad when we were children, particularly my mother, when he'd never come for supper. What was he doing? He was tidying up, sorting out, he was folding up jumpers. I remember him putting the hangers tidy, taking all night to do it. Now there's a bit of me in there. And until fairly recently – I mean I've learnt a bit of sanity in my old age – I haunted the place; you know, I was here all day and all night because I loved it, and perhaps also because I didn't trust the people and I wanted to make sure I did everything myself.

My wife sometimes says, and I deny it (but she's right), that really medicine and my hospital come first. Now, there's no doubt that if my wife's ill or the kids are ill or whatever, I stay at home and I do whatever is necessary. But I don't actually stay at home, I come in as well! The hospital may be relegated to second position very briefly, but it's only briefly, and so most of the time I guess it takes first place in my life and in my thoughts.

What causes aggro is when it's the holidays, and we have a little cottage up in Cumbria, and they say, 'Let's try to set off on Friday', and I say, 'I don't know how I can, I've got a committee meeting and this, that and the other.' Another thing which really causes arguments is that I'm invariably late for dinner parties, and my wife likes to be punctual. Something always happens just as I'm leaving the hospital. And it isn't always a matter of life and death, in fact it rarely is, but it's something I feel *I* can cope with more quickly and more efficaciously. Or the junior staff in casualty have asked me, 'Just before you go, Dr Baderman, would you . . .' and I can't say no. And I never say no. And then when I get home everybody is very tight-lipped, and that upsets me no end and makes me very angry, mainly because I know they're right.

Going back to my father: I have now cut the apron strings, but only at great cost to him and to me. We have great difficulty in speaking and have done for many years, and he's quite unwell, and my mother is very unwell. There's this Jewish thing which I've had since I was a child: 'You're to ring up – twice a week or three times a week' or whatever. And I can't ring them up. I simply can't bring myself to do it. I can't dial the number, my fingers won't work. So my wife does it. She finds it quite difficult as well, but she does it, saintly woman that she is. So I cut the apron strings by limiting the activity and the contact and so forth. I mean, I'm fifty-three. It's only in the last few years that he's stopped telling me to do things. I never did them anyway, but he used to tell me, and it used to anger me.

DR GARETH BEYNON

GERIATRICIAN

━━━━━

I WAS in the army for a couple of years doing National Service before I went to Cambridge. It was the best thing I ever did. You can still tell people who have been in the forces, there's a sense of perspective, maturity, distance. I remember when I started my first house job, one consultant wandered up to me and said, 'You've been in the forces, haven't you? You can always tell.' I was a grammar school boy, I'd not been away to school, and it threw me in with a wide variety of people. I was in the ranks for a year and I was an officer for six months, so I saw it from both sides and learnt a tremendous amount about people, and really clinical medicine is all about people.

I started on a fairly conventional path. I did some general medicine after my house jobs, I became a medical registrar. But I was married, my first child was on the way; I was very short of money. And I was tempted into general practice for the financial security really. I went into an extraordinarily high-powered general practice in Surrey; there were three of us, a real high-flying crowd we were.

I found it very demanding; I found it ultimately demoralizing. I was ill-equipped to deal with the vast amount of psychosomatic and psychological and psychosocial illness that is thrown at you – I was not trained as a GP, I was trained as a hospital doctor. In a way I was very good at general practice, I was very popular, but that's not always a good sign actually. It was exciting at times, I mean, as a GP you are called out to see a sick young woman or a sick child, and you are the first person there, it all rests with you, and I was good at that and I enjoyed it. But the unremitting grind of it, and the fact that mid-thirties you were doing a job where you could see at sixty-five you'd be doing exactly the same thing – getting up to treat influenza at four in the morning – well, I got no kick out of that.

I wasn't intuitively a GP. The split working day always upset me too; I like to come in, start work and, doesn't matter what time I finish, I like to work through. I like the corridors of hospitals, I like the nurses, I like the gossip and the politics.

Things went badly wrong after a while. I had some kind of mid-life crisis; I became ill, and after that I felt I'd got my career perspectives all wrong – I was unhappy out of hospital medicine. So at the late age of about thirty-six, after five or six years of general practice, I decided to come back into hospital medicine, and I thought I'd choose a discipline that involved general medicine and brought in the experience I'd had looking after elderly people in general practice. So I just stuck a pin in the *BMJ*, and arrived at the Middlesex Hospital as a senior registrar in geriatrics. I was very nervous, I'd been out of hospital medicine for a long time, and I was coming back to a major teaching hospital where I'd never worked before. But I fell on my feet. It's like being in a good school or a good regiment, a good teaching hospital, or it was in those days, and it was just what I needed.

I did geriatrics because I felt it would suit my level of experience at that stage. And I just happened to walk into a situation which was ripe for development, the opportunities were there. You see, geriatrics is a very Cinderella discipline; it was rare in those days to have any geriatric beds in a teaching hospital at all. People didn't really know what geriatricians were, didn't understand how to handle the elderly, how they were different from general physicians. And what happened was that by dint of energy and hard work and enthusiasm, we began to develop our unit, started a multi-disciplinary teaching programme, teaching students from OT (occupational therapy), physiotherapy, nursing and medicine. It sounds very straightforward; in fact, it was very avant garde and still is really. And we fought to expand the number of geriatric beds, and this gave me great satisfaction.

Geriatrics is the general medicine of old age. A geriatric patient is an old person who is ill and unable to fend for himself or herself. You can be geriatric at fifty-five or eighty-five. The level of disability is in the eye of the beholder really. I think possibly in some cases it takes a professional to recognize that someone is disabled. It's a very difficult cut-off point to define. In hospital we tend to define it by age, which is crude and arbitrary, and can cause a lot of emotional hardship. You see, if you say everyone over sixty-five is geriatric, quite clearly that's nonsense. And if you say everyone over seventy-five is geriatric, that's nonsense too. What you can say is that more people over seventy-five will be geriatric than others: i.e. the majority of people over seventy-five will need the attention of a geriatrician if they're ill.

You can have a perfectly fit *compos mentis* eighty-year-old driving her Mini, like she has done every day for the last twenty years to do her shopping, who has a traffic accident or falls over, say when she's shopping, and breaks her hip, and that can set off a cycle of events that within forty-eight hours renders her a 'geriatric'. This is because all body organs age, and you get a knock-on effect. It's like a car with 50 or 60,000 miles on the clock, things start going wrong. What appears to be a perfectly functioning social animal one day, falls over and is geriatric in forty-eight hours. Dependent. Mental confusion. A little bit of incontinence. Early chest infection. Thin skin. Early pressure area. This can all happen. And then the neighbours say, 'Poor Muriel, you would never have believed it, and now she's lying in the hospital bed.' She's fractured her femur, she bleeds around the fracture, she's anaemic, the anaemia may precipitate a bit of coronary insufficiency, she might go into heart failure, she lies in bed, she doesn't clear her lung secretion, she develops a bit of bronchial pneumonia, she becomes hypoxic, and suddenly those thickened arteries that have just been coping before to give a perfect social façade are no longer getting the blood round to the brain. She's in a strange place, strange lights, strange environment, she becomes very confused. And so when my mother, who's elderly herself, says about her neighbour, 'Isn't she wonderful? Isn't she marvellous?' in the back of your mind you know she's going to fall over on the ice – all elderly are vulnerable.

If you're age seventy-five and you bust your hip, and the chap at the end of the bed before your operation is a geriatrician, you should be bloody relieved. It's when you're seventy-five and you've bust your hip and the chap who's assessing you medically before your operation isn't a geriatrician – that's the time to be very alarmed. Because the geriatrician looks at things in a very different way. For example, the physician looks for a specific medical diagnosis; a geriatrician looks at the person as a complete person, looks at the patient's social background, psychiatric background, level of dependency – he's looking for failure of recent memory, disturbances of habit, of dress or appearance, of gait and speech and vision – the geriatrician takes a global view of the elderly sick patient. He can't do it himself; he needs his team, he needs his social workers, physios, O Ts, nurses. There are very few true general physicians like us left; they're all specialists in something or other.

In a well-run geriatric ward the spirit and morale is high. Given adequate nursing levels, good leadership, and interesting medicine, morale is excellent, very happy. Given poor leadership, and low nursing ratios, because you need a lot of nurses for the more dependent patients, then morale can plummet alarmingly. Nursing level is very important. Morale in my unit three years ago was sky high, we had a PhD in nursing who was running a superb nursing unit; but things have gone down since. Now, this teaching hospital has never ever been short of nurses until last year, and now we're actually short of nurses – and we can't function without nurses; I mean, it's the death of everything if you've got no nurses. One of my two wards is closed because I haven't got enough nurses. So the waiting list grows and my patients don't get treated. So my patients die.

Not a high enough proportion of the gross national product is devoted to the Health Service. If you put more money into it you could provide more – there's no doubt about that. But the government has decided no. Someone's got to decide priorities. I think the B M A, of which I was an official in the past, are playing a scandalously low profile. I don't understand why really.

The National Health in the 1960s was a beautiful thing, and that is being slowly strangled out of existence. I suspect that within a year or two, if it's as unremitting as this, I shall become very disenchanted indeed. It's all too easy to throw in the towel and say, 'Look, I don't want to be chairman of *this* any more, I regard it as a complete waste of time', but I'm getting very near to that now. Very near indeed.

I mean, there's widespread publication of beds closing, health authorities in trouble, closures, closures, closures. What the hell's it all about? I don't know. I've been committed to the N H S, I've tried very hard, and I've enjoyed it. It's done a lot for me as well, but I've had enough, or very, very nearly had enough. I tried very hard over the last year as chairman of the Middlesex Medical Committee; I work closely with a colleague who's a unit general manager, and he's had enough. I would give it another year, perhaps less, six months, and if there's no improvement, I'm going to call it a day and say, 'Well, do your worst.'

I don't work as hard now as I did. It's not burn-out, but I've found events totally dispiriting. I was very shaken when my superb unit was, through political events that no one really could control, very threatened, and it has never really recovered. I certainly lost a lot of drive there.

There's always got to be a plan B around the corner, particularly the way things are. Perhaps it goes back to the army. The army was a waste of time in many ways, but it taught you a lot of things; they taught you to put things down on paper, and I always teach my senior registrars: one-year plan, five-year plan, ten-year plan. And that should apply to your personal life as well as your professional career. And I just wonder if I might say, 'Let's have another crack at general practice' and continue one or two of my other interests.

I desperately try to avoid getting typecast and settled in my ways. I see too many of my colleagues grow old very quickly in front of my eyes, and I desperately want to avoid that. I see men worn down, particularly in their mid-fifties; they become shells, grey shells, just mechanically going through their day. For Christ's sake, I don't want that. Even if it means going out and retiring to a cottage and doing some part-time general practice I'll do that, rather than become like the zombies that I see.

PROFESSOR COLIN BLAKEMORE

PHYSIOLOGIST

THE GMC recommendations on medical education say that physiology and anatomy and biochemistry shall be the core of pre-clinical teaching for medical students, supplemented where possible by a number of other subjects including psychology, behavioural science, medical sociology, genetics and so on. The implication is that a foundation of understanding of how the body is organized is essential to understand how it goes wrong in clinical conditions.

Physiology looks at how the whole system works together. The foundation of modern physiology really started at the beginning of the last century in France with Claude Bernard, who invented the concept of homeostasis – balanced, self-regulating systems by which the internal systems of the body are maintained at equilibrium. You can't have a self-regulating system without a number of components which are playing off against each other. So physiology is concerned with how systems interact, and the interplay of all these things are what physiology is about. And you can tell the same kind of story for anything which is regulated and kept constant in the body: the amount of glucose in the blood, the size and development of the muscles, the temperature of the body, the salt level in the body, the total fluid volume inside the body. For each of those things you require an explanation which involves hormones, which involves the nervous system, which involves the two or three different organ systems like the kidney and the heart. And it is very complex in its balance.

Let's take the heart. The anatomists would be interested in the structure of the chambers and the valves and how they work as mechanical devices, and maybe how the flow of electricity across the heart influences the way it pumps. In other words, the heart simply as a mechanical and hydro-dynamic organ.

But at another level, a higher level, the physiologist would be interested in how the heart fits into the whole circulation system, what it is responding to, what regulates it, how circulating hormones and adrenaline affect it, and how the return of blood to the heart affects its capacity to pump, and so on.

In most places the essential pre-clinical course is five or six terms, and of that probably something like a third is pure physiology. Here at Oxford it is three lectures a week pretty much continuously through the whole of those five terms and practical work as well, so it is a very considerable load.

One's perspective on the age of students changes as one gets older, but they seem incredibly young to me these days. When there was National Service, I think that did produce a different breed of students who were more mature, more in touch with the world. I remember before I went to Cambridge, I hitch-hiked around the States on my own, and had done all sorts of things which I think broadened my mind and were very informative and influenced my future life too.

But there is tremendous pressure on students these days to get through as quickly as possible, and the government is so concerned to save money on everything that I can't see us reintroducing the luxury of third years in the sixth form or a four-year degree course, the kinds of things that would produce better-rounded people. The medical students are extremely bright – the qualifications for getting into medical school now are horrendously high – but a real worry is that the vocational side of the inspiration to do medicine seems almost to have been lost; medicine is becoming more and more academic all the time. But there must be a balance between intellectual performance and vocation, and we have lost that balance in my view. Schools now are inclined to say, 'My God, you are so good academically you might have a chance of doing medicine', without the pupil playing any part in that decision. The view is that medicine is a secure, high-status profession which is to be prized for that reason.

Even in my day it was true that medics were the hardest worked of all the undergraduates in Cambridge. But I can remember many pleasant afternoons on the river, and having plenty of time to play rugby and act, and all those kind of things. There are very few medical students now who can find the time for those things. If you look at the timetable of a medical student, it is totally full from morning till bedtime. We are narrowing them down in so many ways. And some of them discover half way through that they don't want to do it; they have their intellectual interest and enthusiasm beaten out of them by the sheer mass of facts which they are asked to absorb. There is all this bright sparkling young talent there, and, of course, the bottom line is always money; we can't afford the time to let these people indulge their talents and develop them.

Almost everything that our bodies do is done in a similar way by some other creature, and there are very few ways in which man is unique. Our brain is very highly developed, but everything else about our nervous system, our vision, perception, our learning capacities, all of them can be matched at least by monkeys, and to a large extent by very much simpler organisms, like an octopus, which has terribly good vision and can learn very efficiently.

I am interested in how the visual system works, and how it develops in the young animal, and the young baby for that matter. I work on higher mammals, cats and monkeys, which makes me a perfect target for an attack from anti-vivisectionists because it is very easy to paint horrifying, emotive pictures of research in these areas as just useless inquisitiveness for its own sake rather than having any relevance to the clinical condition of man – which is quite disgracefully false.

A good example to illustrate the opposite case is that most of our modern understanding of how nerves work, which is fundamental to our whole knowledge of the brain and the nervous system, how drugs act on nerves, how anaesthetics work, all of that came out of work on – wait for it – the nerve of the squid. Hodgkin and Huxley, who won a Nobel Prize for that work, were interested in how nerves work in their own bodies. They chose something that was big, easy to keep alive in a dish, and easy to manipulate, so they chose the giant nerve fibre of the squid, which is about a millimetre or more in diameter, a huge thing, but the principles they found applied to us.

I have been suffering for the last year from a very well organized and rather frightening campaign against me and my work.

The present campaign began almost a year ago and it takes a number of forms – marches, campaigns – but mainly in the form of articles in anti-vivisectionist magazines. Some newspapers have taken them up, the *Sunday Mirror* ran an article which was essentially a reproduction of something which had been published in an anti-vivisectionist magazine, based on misrepresentation, and out of context quotations to try and paint a picture of research as useless. These articles have been followed by threats, abusive telephone calls, my mail's been intercepted and opened in the post office and messages put inside, I've had suspicious packages sent to the lab – you know, pretend bombs, not real ones so far, thank God. The children have been threatened with blinding and death, and the police have warned their schools that they should be on the look-out that someone might try to kidnap the children. It's very serious.

A few weeks ago they tried to get into a door which they presumed must lead into the animal house, and it didn't; our animal house is very heavily protected, maximum security, which of course just produces the response you would expect from the anti-vivisectionists: 'What have they got to hide? What's all the security for?' It's so ridiculous. You can't win with that kind of argument.

But this kind of attack has had a very big impact on the teaching of medical students. So much so that combined with economic factors, because maintaining an animal house is expensive, it has virtually eliminated contact with animals for preclinical students. And the problem now is that we are sending people out of medical schools who have had no direct intimate contact with living tissue.

What are we doing? Are we really saying that we want our future doctors to have no feel for what tissue is like until they pick up a scalpel for the first time on the body of a human? If they don't get their experience with animals, then they are going to get their experience on people, and is that preferable? The educational value of seeing how whole systems work in a living animal is tremendous. To some extent one can mimic that with well-made video material, and we use videos a great deal in our teaching, but ultimately it doesn't show the truth.

When I was a medical student a very large proportion of our practical work was done on whole, anaesthetized, de-cerebrate animals. In my opinion that contact with living tissue was not only educationally valuable in that it gave one an insight as to how the whole body works, which you can never get in the same way from a textbook, but it was also crucially important for people whose next contact with living tissue would be with people.

ANGELA BRIDCUT

PHYSIOTHERAPIST

━━━━━━━━

M Y mother actually looked through the career books for me. I wanted to do something with my hands, a practical job, I didn't want to sit behind a desk being a secretary.

It's very much stressed that people going into physiotherapy actually go round a hospital to see if they like it, because a lot of physiotherapy stuff is pretty horrible. You're dealing a lot with sputum and all that sort of thing – that's expectorated material of saliva and mucus and phlegm, you get it up off people's chests. I remember when I was a student, my first patient nearly made me faint. I was walking along the ward and shown somebody with a swelling in her arm, and I keeled over because it was so swollen – five or six times the normal size. But that was the only thing that has ever made me faint, apart from going into theatre as a student, and you see all the blood and all the chopping about. That sort of thing makes anyone faint.

I look after people who have undergone an amputation because of peripheral vascular disease, which is when your arteries harden up so that the blood is restricted. It's not like when they've had an amputation following a car crash and they come into hospital and their legs are completely mashed up and the surgeon must remove it straight away. With my people, once the decision has been made to have their leg removed, they try and give them two or three days before the operation, so that we, as physiotherapists, can go and assess them and explain everything, because it's our job to explain the rehabilitation process after the operation. We let them practise in a wheelchair, which they will use until they are able to walk on a false leg. You must do the amputation within a week of when it's decided, because the patient can get very toxic, and if gangrene sets in, it could become infected. And we make sure they realize why they need the leg off, because often, although the leg might be discoloured and blue, they may not have a lot of pain – you need a lot of pain to convince somebody that they really need their leg off.

At the same time, you have to be aware of the patients who see the leg is blue and say, 'All right, that's got to come off.' I've got this lady at the moment who's saying that, but I feel she needs to be a bit calmer: it's very easy to say, 'Yes, I'll have it off straight away', but there's a great psychological crisis once you've had it off.

The patient can feel very ill and confused before the operation: you tell them things which they don't remember because they're so distraught, and then you have to explain everything to them all over again afterwards, because they haven't absorbed anything you told them before. So it's very important to explain it to the family, so you can get their support.

You really need two or three days for them to settle down after the operation; they can still be feeling quite confused, they're under a lot of painkillers, and you can get what's called phantom pain, when you think your leg is still there, and of course it's not, it's been cut off below the knee. Once they're up and about on the second day, they start facing life without their leg. And once they can walk confidently on their new leg with whatever walking aid they require, then they can go home. We do lots of visits at their home, check they can manage in their house with a wheel-chair, and check all the facilities.

As long as you can get them home, even if it's just for a month or a few weeks and then they die, they still have gone home and they've left hospital, and their family, if they've got families, are delighted to see them home.

On the one hand, you have to be very involved with the patients. You have to know the ins and outs of their lives in order to work out what's best for them and how they're going to manage at home. You do get to know them really well, because you're fitting their legs for them, you're handling a lot of their body for them; you can't be stand-offish. You're with them for about four or six weeks after their amputation, and you see them twice a day at their home.

On the other hand, you learn not to get too involved. I mean, if somebody has an amputation and the wound doesn't heal, and they go for a further operation and then eventually they die, you're very upset, but you can't be involved. You just can't get too emotional. It's the same as if a patient is dying of cancer, you know they're going to die. And with these amputees, after they have had one amputation, they're likely to have a second within five years of their first amputation, and then there's very limited expectation after that. It all sounds so ghastly, doesn't it?

You have to learn to stand aloof from it emotionally, you have to. If somebody dies, you're upset and you think, 'Oh, what a shame.' Sometimes you say, 'Oh, what a relief', they were in such pain, but you soon learn to adapt and just not think too much about it.

There's a lot of people you can't help because they're going to die, and you have to recognize that, you have to say, 'Right, with that person I'm not going to be able to achieve what I hoped', so you set your sights a bit lower, and work at that. But you're always wanting to get the best you can for your patient.

You hear that they've died, and you do feel sorry, but if you burst into tears over every patient who died, you couldn't do the job, you just couldn't.

But I have fun, I really enjoy it. I much prefer treating the elderly patients to the young; they've got a lot to tell you about life, they're all people who've been through the war, been through a different era to myself. And the people I see now, they've got so much wrong with them, that's why I like looking after them. Most of them are alone, or if they've got a husband or a wife, they might be crippled as well.

You come home feeling very tired, you are literally hauling people around all day. You have to pull them out of a chair and make them walk, and if a physiotherapist doesn't do it, nobody else will – and that physically is very exhausting. This job is exhausting mentally too, but we're a fit breed compared to, say, secretaries sitting on their bums all day typing.

The job's made me hard. I've become very unsympathetic, and that reflects in my social life. Friends' predicaments don't move me; you hear someone has just broken up with their boyfriend, and their problems seem so small. Someone said to me yesterday, 'Don't you have any feelings?'

It's very important to cut yourself off. Occasionally, say on holiday, you might wonder how so and so is getting on, but generally I don't take work home with me; I mean, there's nothing you can do for the patient while you're not there.

I don't think we're paid enough. We're paid slightly more than nurses, because we are entirely responsible for what we do, whereas nurses act much more under the doctor. We go through a much heavier training. But we don't earn anything during our training, which nurses do, and so you have to be able to support yourself on a grant. And a junior physiotherapist earns a salary which in this day and age isn't adequate.

I've been in my current grade for three years, and I get my next increment in June, and after that, that's it. My salary is stuck then. At the level I'm at now, I've got no further to go except into administration. Instead of looking after one or two staff, I'd be looking after a whole department of up to fifteen, and for all that additional responsibility the money's not worth it. I already have to supplement my income by doing private work at a different hospital at weekends. There's lots of physiotherapists who do other work: they might do physiotherapy, they might do waitressing, anything to supplement their income.

We should get enough money to be able to live. At the age of thirty, you ought not to have come to the end of your career structure salary-wise. I do fell bitter. We're way behind what we should be getting.

PROFESSOR ANTHONY CLARE

PSYCHIATRIST

My background was not medical. My father was a solicitor; he's retired now. I entered medical school in Dublin and in those days you didn't need to indicate whether you were a scientist or a humanities; you took a broad range of subjects right until the age of eighteen, and I can remember very clearly that the choice was between doing English and doing medicine. I decided to do medicine, and I know operating at the back of it all was the notion that it was useful, something that would make some kind of contribution in a way that I didn't think studying English would. There was some notion of service, God help me.

I did have an injury when I was fifteen: horsing around with a friend, I put my left hand through a glass door and severed the median nerve, indeed the major artery to the hand, and I spent some time in hospital. I suppose that was a factor too, in that I was very drawn by the drama of the hospital: the romance and the drama, both really. And I still find hospitals romantic places in many ways, particularly at night, because of that curious mixture of silence and the hint of drama: the nurses, the lights down, with every now and again somebody rushed in, rushed out, a sense of crisis, and yet peaceful. A curious contrast.

The sixties in Ireland, as they were in most places, but particularly there, were really opening up, liberating times, with Kennedy in Washington and John XXIII in Rome, and Ireland was beginning to stagger into the twentieth century, and this all had an impact on the university, and psychiatry seemed of all the subjects related in some curious way to that. Laing was writing, psychiatry started to become very public. Physicians either embraced psychiatry and regarded it with considerable awe, or they saw it as something really impenetrable. But outside of medicine, psychiatry was seen as an interesting subject. The rest of medicine, I have to tell you, at the beginning of the 1960s looked as if it had solved everything. There was a tremendous feeling of confidence in renal medicine, in metabolic and clinical medicine, and that if it hadn't solved things, it was on its way. Funny how things change.

Psychiatry is the branch of medicine that's devoted to the study of . . . the old phrase used to be 'mental disease'; I suppose we now call it 'psychopathological disturbance', or 'disorder', 'psychiatric ill-health', 'mental malfunction' – all these words are interchangeable. It differs from psychology in the sense that psychology is the study of normal mental function, and I suppose psychiatry is the study of abnormal mental function.

The criteria of illness are that there is a disturbance in function, the autonomy of the individual is impaired, he cannot by himself restore himself to health – that's what makes it a disease. The diabetic, even though he knows he has diabetes, cannot restore himself back to health, he can participate in the process but he cannot do it of his own accord. Likewise people who get depressed: it is impossible for the individual under his or her own steam to restore that mood to normal. I mean, you and I when we get low, we go off to the pictures or we read a book or we watch television or whatever. And many depressed patients will initially try that and find it fails, and it moves into the remit of an illness.

If I'm teaching students, I teach them a spectrum of illness; so, for example, at the severe end of the spectrum are the severe mental illnesses, the psychoses, which usually involve a break with reality, people who see things or believe or experience things which are out of the normal ken of an ordinary individual. And the two major psychoses would be schizophrenia and manic depressive illness, and the organic psychoses are things like the deliriums, dementia, and the brain disorders that affect psychological health.

Then, if you move back along the spectrum, you're arriving at the severe neuroses, which themselves merge into the moderate and the mild neuroses. Now, these are conditions that are different from the psychoses in the sense that they tend to be exaggerations of what you and I and everyone else ordinarily feels. We all feel anxious and depressed and to some extent a little obsessional, and sometimes compulsively driven, but the severe end of this neurotic spectrum can be very crippling disorders indeed – people who are utterly impaired by these neurotic states.

And then there's a group of conditions which are really quite a problem, the so-called personality disorders. And these are people who don't so much manifest symptoms as show disturbances in the way their personality has developed; the layman would think of the more cold-blooded psychopath who just seems to have learnt no moral responsibility. But there are other forms of personality disorders: there are people who've got a very poor tolerance for stress, are very inadequate, find it very difficult to cope, are extremely hypochondriacal over many years, and these conditions develop in adolescence, indeed the layman recognizes them as personalities rather than as illness. And one reason that they're a problem is that no one really knows who should be treating them. Many of them come into conflict with the law, and so the penal system sees them, but doesn't think they're really appropriate for them, and medicine and psychiatry also are brought into contact with them, and haven't as yet got terribly effective methods of managing them. But they are part and parcel, at the moment at any rate, of the psychiatric sphere of influence.

Then there are the addictions, which we're also involved in, addictive behaviours, drugs, alcohol, gambling, one or two other pathological addictions.

I'm simplifying greatly, but I would think that the consensus now would be that for the severe mental illnesses there's a very significant genetic component. And for the neuroses, it looks, while there might be a genetic component, as if the social and environmental contribution seems to be more significant.

If you look at this great array of medical specialties in the latter half of the twentieth century, there is a growing realization within the profession, and particularly outside it, that the neglect of behavioural and psychological aspects of medicine is one of the single greatest deficiencies of contemporary medicine, and so in a sense it's an exciting time to be a psychiatrist. The brain has really been extraordinarily neglected.

I think the public in the twenty-five years I've been in psychiatry have steadily grown more interested in it, although they're still rather fearful and ignorant about it. There was a tendency for psychiatrists and psychologists to speak complex jargon which rather mystified people in a way. Doctors do it all the time, of course, but they get away with it because they're regarded as scientists. But even they have got to start making things understandable. That's the democracy in which we now live; the smallest in the land demand to be able to understand the biggest, and that's fair enough.

I worry at the extent to which we're not just a scientifically illiterate society – we've always been that – but now I'm worrying that we're becoming illiterate across the board. Let me give you an example of what I mean. At the end of the day, one of the absolutely crucial aspects of being a doctor is that the clinician should rely very heavily on facilitating the patient to describe what is going wrong and how they see it. Now, I think that calls for a literacy, an understanding of communication, an articulacy and a curiosity about people which I suspect fifty years ago most doctors had because they had to rely on that almost entirely; there were no lab machines, CT scanners and so on. What's happened is that the development of machines has meant that more and more our doctors are reading signals from machines and are not frightfully good at tapping what is still the fundamental source of information, the patient. I think that's sad.

Why do doctors hoard knowledge? One reason is because they realize that the amount they know isn't all that massive. There's a feeling that the public is better off not knowing. But people do want to know; after all, their bodies are at the end of the day the one thing that belongs to them. I think it's bad that the medical profession has not taken enough account of the need to get people to know more, to know the limits of medicine, to know the potential of the body and its limits, to know that man is a fallible machine, that disease, you might say, is almost the more natural state of man than health.

I mean, in one sense all of nature's flawed, if you want to use the notion of flaw meaning anything that has a defect or a potential to disease. If you're someone who gets depressed by defect, don't go into medicine. Go on to the wards and you begin to wonder how do people *normally* function? You see every system with disturbances. But defect is the very essence of medicine; medicine is about defect. That's why doctors become either rather cynical or hypochondriacal.

There's a sort of late-twentieth-century feeling that man is perfect and all these bloody flaws should be eradicated. There was a wonderful example of this the other night on the TV, when a woman in a Gloucestershire village where there's been an outbreak of meningitis said, 'For God's sake, they've been studying this for months! They should have come up with the answer!' And that's very much twentieth-century man. In fact, meningitis is a mysterious condition, still: we know what causes it, but we don't know how it spreads.

And the media are invariably drama-orientated, which I can understand, but it is a problem. There is a tendency to concentrate on the more dramatic end of the spectrum. They will give hundreds of column inches to, say, a liver transplant, and very little to the less dramatic, more painstaking developments. It skews people into thinking that that's what medicine is about. It skews money in that direction; the public will put their hands in their pockets for cardiac surgery and cancer and so on, and will neglect things like geriatrics, psychiatry, mentally handicapped – well, ordinary routine general medical care.

The brain is where the material and the non-material coincide. We know that thoughts are immaterial, but they may have a material basis. I mean, how does a thought affect a brain function? We know it can, because a sexual thought can cause you to have an erection, and yet, what is that thought? I tease medical students with this, 'What is that thought?' And they say, 'Well, it's the product of enzymes interacting . . .' and so on, but they realize that that's not really an explanation, it's just another level of description. And there's a danger, of course, that what many doctors do is they either become materialists or else they stay as very rational scientists and then they have this elaborate, utterly detached, metaphysical explanation for life and death, and they never try and relate the two. Maybe that's the only way you can survive, I don't know. At the moment all I can say is I suspect that unravelling the secrets of the brain is not just a scientific quest. I think unlocking the secrets of consciousness will be a step on the road towards understanding existence and whether in fact there is an external agency involved in existence, or whether this is a material world and consciousness is a material evolution.

As we unlock, unravel, there is a possibility that we will see an order and an organization in nature and existence that can only be explained by recourse to a God. On the other hand, we may not. I mean, I'm an agnostic, I think at the end of the day you come to religious belief through faith. You cannot scientifically prove the existence of God, and if you could, then there would be no such thing as religious faith. So at the moment there are two spheres very wide apart – religion and science – but in unravelling the brain there is something religious about the quest; you really are looking at the nature of creativity.

Because what is the brain? Your brain is the residue of your unique personal experience, your memories, your environment; it stores all the things that I as a psychiatrist am interested in. We know that we could take your kidney out and put another kidney in, and you remain as you were. But take your brain out and put someone else's brain in, and then you're not John Smith, you're the body of John Smith with somebody else's brain.

Put it this way: when we have sorted out the liver and the kidney, and the heart and the lungs, we will have despatched the offal – that's the human body in comparison with the brain. The way in which mind and matter integrate and create is the fundamental mystery of life. And the brain is the only organ that truly commands all. I mean, to watch the workings of the kidney is a miracle of nature, but the brain is in a different order. And unravelling the brain is going to take – I was going to say a lifetime – it's going to be an eternity, I suspect, and we're only beginning.

DR JOHN COLLINS

CHEST SPECIALIST

———

BREATHING is a very natural act which requires very little conscious input from the healthy person. What happens is the message goes from your brain to the rib cage and the diaphragm to expand the lungs, the chest wall moves out, the belly moves down and your lungs expand, and then when they have filled up with air, you let it all go and breathe out.

The diaphragm is a curious thing. It is rather like sheets of white tissue, like you see in meat from the butcher separating one muscle bundle from another: that is called fascia, and it is predominantly made of a chemical, fibrous substance called collagen. The centre of the diaphragm is a broad sheet of fascia, with muscle strips around its edges, just like springs around the edge of a trampoline, tying it to the lower few ribs and the spine at the back, and it bulges upwards against the heart and the lungs, arching over the stomach, liver and spleen. If you are taking a maximum breath, two-thirds to three-quarters of that breath is due to the diaphragm pulling down, pushing your guts and lungs down and expanding them

The lungs have a glistening pale surface. In an infant or child, they will be very pink, but if you have reached mature years and lived in an urban environment, they will look greyish because of the amount of carbon pigment that has got deposited. Country dwellers tend to have pink lungs compared with town dwellers. In an average 5 foot 10 inch man they would have a total capacity of about six and a half litres. A woman will tend to have 15–20 per cent less lung than a man in ratio to height.

In normal breathing, as you and I are speaking to each other, for example, we are probably using about half a litre of breath per breath, half a litre in, half a litre out. If we walk briskly along the road, we are breathing twenty-five litres minimum, and if we are running, we are probably breathing 100 to 150 litres a minute, so it goes up enormously, and similarly the number of breaths you take will go up.

There are two lungs, situated in the chest cavity on either side of the heart. The right-hand lung has three lobes stacked on top of each other, each of which is a wedge shape. On the left-hand side, because of the presence of the heart, there are only two lobes, with a similar triangular arrangement, one on top of the other. The lungs operate passively: they are just stuck to the chest by surface tension and expanded by the chest expanding.

Lungs are very prone to problems; 30 per cent of the population will die of a lung cause. Lung cancer is the commonest cause of death in England after coronary artery disease. It is said that 25 per cent of hospital admissions with real illness, as opposed to 'let's have a look at you' type of admission, are due to lung disease.

You have two clearance systems to get germs back up again. The crudest one is cough. Cough is a mechanism by which the system says, 'Here is a foreign particle, wrap it up in sticky stuff and blast it out', so you cough it up. The other one is a continuous process. All the way from the mouth and nose down to the very end of the tube system, the whole of the respiratory tract is lined by cilia, waving hairs which beat in beautiful unison. And they sweep in a way which is not yet understood, but they are actually synchronized so they all beat together and they are bringing a continuous stream of fluid back up to the larynx and to the mouth. But it is so small in quantity that you don't even have to clear your throat and cough, it just comes up into your mucus and you swallow it. It is then taken away through your bowel.

The reason why we get so many respiratory infections is the fact that germs have ready access to the lungs and get down pretty easily. The tremendous amount of air with its foreign substances that you take in every day, something like 10,000 litres of air or maybe more, exposes the tube system to an enormous number of insults. The basis for lung damage in cigarette smoking is almost certainly the inhalation of carcinogenic substances, which leads to lung cancer. I always tell smokers and asthmatics that they are my guarantee of employment into the twenty-first century.

MR ALAN CROCKARD
NEUROSURGEON

I CAN never really remember a time when I didn't want to become a doctor. I spent the first ten or eleven years of my life in Nigeria, where my parents were missionaries. My mother was a nurse, and my father and my mother did the best they could for the people that were sick, and I used to enjoy dressing wounds and that sort of thing.

When I went back to school in Northern Ireland, the Royal Belfast Academical Institution, in my interview the headmaster asked me, 'What do you want to do?' And I said, 'I want to be a doctor', and I can remember him remarking that it was unusual for a young boy to be so clear as to what he wanted to do.

I suppose I got into neurosurgery because I enjoyed the manual skills of it, in the same way as dressing wounds if you like, and as a student I spent a lot of time watching surgery, which I found fascinating. When someone went sick in the neurosurgery ward, I was asked to go and do a locum in that ward. It frightened me silly: first day, two people died, someone else had an epileptic fit, but I suppose what impressed me about the people who were my mentors was that they were calm in the face of all these problems. And another thing I liked, although neurosurgeons are skilled operators, they depend very heavily upon their diagnostic abilities, and so I thought 'This is for me.'

The brain occupies the whole of our skull from the forehead right to the back of the head, and weighs about 1,500 grammes, one and a half kilos, and it's pulsating with every heartbeat and every time you breathe. It's a sort of creamy yellow colour, and there are little hills and hollows on the surface of the brain, and in amongst these there are the blood vessels, and you can tell the difference between an artery and a vein quite easily because the arteries are bright red and the veins are dark blue, the oxygen having been extracted by the brain. The blood going through the brain gives it a certain rigidity, but because it's surrounded by a fine, almost cobweb-like membrane covering called the pia arachnoid, it would be the consistency of, say, Flora margarine, but once you part the covering membranes, it's more firm than that.

Because I do a lot of surgery, I physically look at the brain or the spinal cord about four if not five days a week. The scenarios that I would be involved in are people who've had an accident, or where there's a clot pressing on the brain, and one would have to take that clot out, like for someone who's had a brain haemorrhage from something like an aneurysm, which is a weakness of a blood vessel wall, or to remove a tumour. Brain cancer is very common – not as common as lung or breast cancer, but still one of the major killers.

There are areas where it is very important not to touch, or you touch very carefully, such as the brainstem, for example, the bit at the back joining the brain to the spinal cord: it's close to the nerves that work respiration and heart, so touching that roughly could mean that the patient might never breathe again. On the left side, just above the ear in right-handed people, is where speech is, and if you handle that roughly, the person may never speak again. So clearly one has to know one's way around and know the areas where it is relatively safe to make an incision to get into the brain to do whatever you have to do, and so a detailed knowledge of the anatomy and the physiology are a prerequisite.

If you said to me, where exactly is it that makes a violinist be a wonderful violinist instead of just being someone who can read music – that sort of relationship is something about which we have little knowledge. But those are the sort of pathways that we're now exploring.

There are minute differences from one brain to another, the

little ridges, the gyri and sulci, do vary ever so slightly. Now with the scanner we can look at a brain and say: that's predominantly a right-handed brain, or this is a left-handed brain, although they were originally thought to be perfectly symmetrical.

The brain is packed away in a very solid little box, and tightly compartmented, so that you can hit your head without damaging the brain. To get in for an operation, we actually have to make a drill hole and then use some form of power saw to lift a piece of skull out of the way to get in and look at it. So you need skills of carpentry, which require a degree of physical strength, and then when you're handling the brain, there has to be a degree of delicacy because of the material with which you're working.

I have developed a new technique, the trans-oral operation, which is a new way of reaching things at the base of the brain. It requires a fair bit of manual dexterity, but it is very exciting. Imagine something at the bottom of a suitcase that you want to get at: you have to lift everything out, put your hand in, take out the 5p piece, or whatever it was at the bottom of your suitcase, and put everything back in again. But we've developed the technology to go through the mouth to the base of the brain. You see, the base of the brain is just lying there on a piece of bone: if you put your finger in your mouth and feel the back of your throat, there's a piece of bone there – if you touch it, it may make you feel sick. That piece of bone is the topmost vertebra of your neck, and going a little further up, that is the bone at the base of the skull. And on the other side of that is the brainstem, where those vital centres I was telling you about are. So rather than lift it up and get at it from behind, we can now do that going from the front, and that seems to have caught the imagination.

In many ways it's a very exciting time, because I think the brain is where heart and heart surgery were twenty-five years ago, when they developed the tools and began to understand how to work out the operations, we can use drugs as markers and localize their action in the brain; for the first time you can actually see what's happening – so I would say that the next twenty-five years for the brain are going to be very exciting.

MR ELLIS DOUEK
EAR, NOSE AND THROAT SPECIALIST

═══════

WELL, the proper Latin name for the combined specialties of diseases of the ear, nose and larynx is otorhinolaryngology, but as that's a mouthful, people refer to them as 'ear, nose and throats' and therefore 'ENT'. They're connected anatomically in that they're all three developed from the same bits of the pharynx in the embryo, and a lot of the diseases go together. Not so much now, in that we deal with very complex things like cancer of the throat, which really has little to connect it to cancer of the ear. And we deal with deafness, a great deal of which is related not to embryologic origin at all but to an out pouch of the brain which forms the inner ear.

Medical students all come knowing vaguely that they want to be doctors. And then, very early in their career, by the second year, virtually, everyone knows whether he wants to be a surgeon or not. Those who want to be surgeons see somebody doing beautiful surgery, and they feel, 'Oooh, this is lovely, this is art. I want to do this'.

Having decided that I wanted to be a surgeon, I felt that a lot of abdominal surgery was very gross. It didn't interest me that much. Cardiac surgery, which was just coming in, didn't have the sort of intellectual interest that I felt I needed. I wanted to study the human soul, that was really interesting – what else is there in life? But the soul is a bit inaccessible. So then I wanted to study the brain, how that works. But the brain surgeons, they remove a big tumour and then you have a patient who is hardly able to walk, and they would call that a 'great success'. So I decided that what was really interesting was to study the human senses, and that is what allows you to really understand how the brain functions. And in ENT you can study hearing, you can study balance, you can study smell, you can study taste, you can study touch, and the senses in the end decide how the brain works. And this is the way I look at it.

In the past, ENT surgeons couldn't do appendicectomy or gastrectomy, so the real work of those surgeons meant drainage of abscesses from the abdomen and from the chest, and they really only dealt with infection, that's all there was. So for people who formed huge abscesses, they would drain them: some survived, most died. You see, the type of surgery that can be done now is because infection isn't a problem; you bathe people in antibiotics and this allows you to do the most extensive surgery.

Oscar Wilde died of the mastoid infection; they weren't able to operate and drain it in time. But ironically, the person who actually started operations for drainage of the mastoid bone was Oscar Wilde's father, Sir William Wilde, and his descendants are still practising ENT surgeons in Ireland.

The rough type of surgeons who practised in the eighteenth century just dealt with the throat. Then you got a period where lenses had been invented, and so you got people peering into the ear. Of course, they had to do this with gas light, but they still could do it, they were good at mirrors and lenses. Not long after, somebody in Italy, I think he was a singing master, learnt to look at the larynx by holding out a mirror and heating it up a bit so that when you breathed it didn't fog over, and he started inspecting the vocal chords of the singers, and this took off, and surgeons began to look at the vocal chords of people who complained of hoarseness, and when they saw tumours and things, they would start making grabs at them with bent forceps and various crude instruments. There was no anaesthesia.

Before the Second World War, there was nothing that you could do about deafness – except shout. After the war, you had hearing aids, because electronics came into being in amplification.

You could also operate on the middle ear, the three little bones that vibrate and transmit vibrations. No one had ever dreamed that this would be possible. There were a few very far-sighted people who had tried, but they failed because people developed infections. Now we could control infection with antibiotics and, with microscopes of tremendous power so that we could operate on the middle ear, take out the little bones, replace them with plastic ones. So that was a tremendous advance.

However, in medicine nothing seems adequate, because as soon as we could cope with all this, the main problem seemed to be those who had nerve deafness. And as you couldn't cure this, you had to say, 'Well, I'm afraid that nothing can be done.' Yet now, my own research group is implanting electronic devices on the nerve, and if you stimulate this with electricity, the brain perceives it as sound – and we're now trying to make it meaningful sound.

By the end of this century, we'll have made some advances, but in twenty-five years, what we're doing now will seem unbelievably laborious, and I think by that time, there will hardly be anybody with a hearing loss who couldn't be cured.

The strange thing is that many patients when they come to see me are not quite aware that I am the surgeon as well. There's a class aspect to this. I'm at Harley Street one day and a half a week, the rest of my time I'm at Guy's Hospital, so I see all sorts – could be a king, or a prime minister on Monday, could be a cleaner from Southwark tomorrow morning. The middle class will ask you, 'Will you be doing the operation?' hoping that you will, because they've been told, 'Try and go and see *him* because he's good at that particular thing.' They are very anxious that you are doing the operation. If not, they want to know who will cut them up. The working class is the contrary. If you say, 'I am going to do the operation', they often look at you with suspicion, almost horror, because they see a rather plump, middle-aged man – it's not their dream surgeon; they want somebody who is gowned and masked and comes from heaven and does the operation and disappears. Many people would look at me and say, 'I'm not going to let that chap cut me up. He's just an ordinary man. I want a God to do this!'

There are few things more ritualistic than surgery. The whole thing is a ritual from beginning to end. It starts with the patient being brought down from the ward by a nurse, the ward nurse hands over the patient formally to the nurse in the operating theatre. You could say the ritual even starts the day before with the anaesthetist seeing them and prescribing the premedication, which is given an hour before, always exactly an hour, although if you gave it an hour and five minutes or three-quarters of an hour it wouldn't make any difference. But the ritual is that it's an hour. You come into the operating theatre, which has its own ritual: the surgeon scrubs his hands – of course he scrubs his hands, because you've got to be clean if you're going inside people – but remember the symbolic aspects of hand washing which are part of all religions; and then there's the gowning, and the people who are operating, being sterile, have to be helped on and tied into these gowns. So immediately there's the ritual of the team involvement, one person has been given this role of simply tying you up behind, and to help you on with your gloves. I have a mild allergy to a particular type of glove, so the right make is there. If the wrong one is there, you're thrown! Of course, it's no big deal, you could just say, 'Look, I don't like the Region gloves, I like the Biogel.' But it somehow interrupts the whole process, and everything seems to go better, your mood is built up by having all these things go right – the right gloves, the right person to tie you on. Then you come to the operation, and there are perhaps five or six people involved. All of them know their role – you hope they all know! With the crumbling of the system we have now, very often you have nurses who have never worked with you before, and this is very off-putting. One orthopaedic surgeon I know came out of the operating theatre almost in tears. He said he came in and the nurse, a young nurse, asked him what size gloves he wore. And he said to me, 'But I've been operating here for twenty years! I mean, how can anyone ask me that?' I told him, 'Look, it's no big deal.' But it was quite clearly part of the ritual that had slipped up, and rather thrown him.

Then you get ready for the operation. The nurse is standing in the right position, everything is done according to the ritual. At that point I take the knife and I cut my incision behind the ear. Now, part of the ritual is that the nurse knows what instruments you're going to use next, so she will give you a retractor (everything in the right order), and then I may have to go right through the bone, and I will need a drill for this. So she will give me the right drill, and so on. The more correct things given to you according to the ritual, the more confident you feel, supported by people that know what they're doing.

It's less physically strenuous than, say, the cardiac surgeon cutting through the sternum, or the orthopaedic surgeon sawing bones, but it's more strenuous in that you have to be so precise and do it through a microscope. But it's exhilarating. I can spend a whole afternoon and evening in the operating theatre, and I feel very good. I find it much more wearying spending the day talking to patients – which I find very wearying, and not at all exhilarating.

If you take any group of specialists in anything, you imagine there are going to be shared characteristics because this is what guided them in that direction. For instance, when I started in E N T, there were many extremely rough, almost disgusting E N T surgeons who you felt were butchers, because a lot of the work that they did was on that sort of level, you know, just people who removed tonsils and that's all they did, and it didn't require any major intellectual considerations. But the people we have now are often very sensitive people. You could say a cancer surgeon needn't be a sensitive person, but imagine you're dealing with somebody who has cancer of, say, the larynx. If you're to have any chance of cure, you have to remove his throat, and he will be breathing through a hole in the windpipe, and will never be able to speak. Many of these people may be old men. You have to ask yourself things like, how long is he going to live if I do this? Is his life going to be worth living?

By and large ENT surgeons are very nice people. You don't get the terrible sort of disputes that you see in some other specialties where people are very grand and don't speak to each other. ENT surgeons on the whole get on well together, they're not competitive in that sense. Intellectually they're at a high level, they're very artistic, and musically inclined. I mean, if I go to Covent Garden, I'm as like as not going to meet three or maybe four ENT surgeons.

DR RICHARD ELLIS

ANAESTHETIST

─────

IF you really want to know, looking back on it, I think I became a doctor through lack of initiative. My father was a doctor, his father had been a doctor, and my brother and I grew up with the idea, without any coercion or compulsion, that one of us would be a doctor. And my brother, who is a little older than I, came back and said one day he wanted to be an accountant, and I just said, 'Right, well I'll be the doctor.' I mean, that's how the career choice was made, there wasn't any sort of burning ambition at that stage to heal people, or anything like that.

The anaesthetist prepares somebody for operation, sends them off to sleep in a pleasant sort of way, looks after them while the operation or whatever is going on, makes sure that potentially harmful or life-threatening effects of that operation are negated, and the patient wakes up comfortably afterwards. That part of the anaesthetic, which is going off to sleep, is known as induction of anaesthesia. We've got a menu of about six agents that are commonly used, and we would select one of those to achieve the transition pleasantly and smoothly from being fully awake to fully asleep and unaware for the duration of the operation. And the analogy I always think rather apposite is that if you look at a symphony orchestra, there aren't that many instruments, there are a few fiddles and a few trumpets and that sort of thing, but the range of music a limited number of instruments can produce is infinite, and that, I think, is virtually the same approach to the impedimenta of anaesthesia. The techniques we have are essentially limited, but with various combinations we can do absolutely anything to look after a patient, to keep him safe while the surgeon does absolutely anything that modern scientific surgery indicates he should do.

And having got the patient to sleep, then we go and do something different to keep him asleep, and that involves a different sequence of techniques which paralyses their voluntary muscles, which sounds rather horrific to a layman but in fact it's a very logical and safe way of administering anaesthesia. And there are a whole variety of muscle relaxants which we might choose. Then we would use analgesic drugs, drugs which diminish the appreciation of pain – classically they're derivatives of opium: morphine or pethidine. Surely, you ask, if the patient is unconscious, he cannot feel pain? But in fact in the midst of being asleep and having a surgeon operating on you, there's a fair amount of reflex activity, because the body resents being attacked, and crudely, a surgical operation is a kind of attack. If I were to lunge at you with a knife, your body would immediately respond by pumping out adrenaline to defend yourself; you have an in-built flight and fight and fear reaction. Well, surgery will excite the same reaction, even though the patient is unconscious, and it's generally accepted in anaesthesia, the patient suffers less of a metabolical upset if these various reflexes have been controlled during his surgery, and that's an additional thing that the anaesthetist has to think about in addition to merely keeping the chap asleep.

So our job is not simply to keep the patient asleep, although that's the perception of anaesthesia: 'This chap gave me a needle and I went to sleep', and they rather hope that we're going to stay for the operation – we always do, but they're never quite sure if we're going to. Hopefully no patient is ever more than an arm's length from his anaesthetist for the whole of the operation.

Let me give you an example of an operation, let's say one I did this morning. There is a condition known as coarctation of the aorta, which is a congenital abnormality and presents quite characteristically in fit young people who have an x-ray when they go from one job to another – say they've had a medical for life insurance. With this condition, the aorta, which is the main blood vessel taking blood from the heart around the body, has become very narrowed, and that means two things: the aorta beyond the narrowing doesn't get very much blood, so all the organs in the bottom of the body, essentially the kidneys and the guts and legs, don't get a great deal of blood; or conversely, the blood going to the top of the body could be under very high pressure.

So the surgeon is going to either enlarge that constriction or he will replace it with some artificial material. And that will involve putting a clamp upstream across the aorta to stop all the blood flow so he can do his operation, which means the bottom of the body is denied blood supply. And that raises one or two problems: with all the output of the heart stopped going further on by the clamp, the pressure in the top of the body rises hugely, and at that stage we could actually be at risk of the patient getting exactly the reason that we're operating for, i.e. sudden cardiac standstill, or he'll bleed into his brain, and that's an enormous risk, and it's down to the anaesthetist to control that set of circumstances.

We use a whole variety of injections into the patient's blood stream to help keep him asleep and keep the harmful effects of the operation at bay. We monitor the patient's progress through-out the whole of the operation, and in an operation like the one we're talking about, the patient would have his blood pressure monitored by what we call an invasive method: instead of taking blood pressure like everybody's probably had done, with a cuff on their arm and a stethoscope, in this circumstance we would actually put a needle into arteries to measure pressure directly at both ends of the body so we can see how both bits are getting on at critical times of the operation. We would also monitor the electrocardiogram, which gives us the rhythm and the rate of the heart, and would also indicate if the patient is liable to develop heart failure during the surgery, which is a possibility. We insert a little tube into the jugular vein, and that gives us an enormous amount of information about the well-being of the heart and how near it is to failing or having some adverse response. To measure the patient's temperature, we put little applicators in the gullet or the oesophagus, which would give us the heart temperature, and possibly on his skin as well, because one can produce a fair amount of information from temperature difference between the middle of you and the outside. And because we've got all these tubes in blood vessels, we can take out samples of the patient's blood and analyse them frequently during the operation for changes in the body's chemistry, because once one allows the changes associated with putting that clamp on to get out of hand, one really is sliding down a slippery slope. So we measure the changes all the time, and as soon as we see any significant changes for the worst occurring, we'll intervene to make them normal. It's a very close observation of the patient.

Well, the patient that I have seen through quite a serious procedure, I guarantee if I said, 'Who was your anaesthetist, do you recognize me?' the fact that he probably wouldn't – even though he met me before the operation and afterwards too – and that he might not fully appreciate the service that I delivered for him . . . well, I don't go home at the end of a working day and get upset. But it would be nice to be appreciated, we all like that. But that's not the main reason one does the job. I know this sounds frightfully pious, but it's more than enough satisfaction to see that at the end of the procedure he ends up safely back in the ward and he's hopefully cured.

Anaesthetists, by and large, we aren't a great macho lot. But we would all dearly like to see people be more aware of the sort of things we do, to see the public perception of anaesthesia become more accurate.

DR RODNEY FOALE

CARDIOLOGIST

WE see some valvular heart disease and some primary heart muscle disease, but by far the majority of patients that come to me have symptoms that suggest coronary heart disease, narrowing of the coronary arteries – and that is the single most common cause of death in this country. In fact the number of patients dying from coronary heart disease and disorders of the cardiological system shows that for approximately 60 per cent of patients between the ages of forty to eighty, the cause of death will be cardiovascular: principally coronary artery occlusion* causing heart attack, and cerebral artery occlusion causing stroke. It's by far the most devastating single epidemic that has been recognized this century.

There are about sixty full-time practising cardiac consultants in this country. And with a population of 50, 60 million, that is an appalling ratio. In Boston, where I trained, a city of 5, 6 million people, there were fifty or sixty cardiologists in the one hospital.

It's absolutely outrageous, and the worst of it is that these deaths could be prevented by early detection, but the patients that we can repair and send out as normal don't get to us. Cardiologists aren't getting to the nub of the problem in the community: screening and educating on a regular basis, informing their colleagues in general practice or general physicianship what to look for, how to refer early and why. Cardiologists only see the disasters – when you've had your second heart attack and

*Occlusion is closing or closure.

your heart muscle isn't working any more, and you can't get out of the bed, or when you've got such severe arterial disease that the only hope is a surgical operation, for which there's a two-year waiting list.

The understanding of the heart as an organ is zero, and therefore the understanding of the problems that affect the heart is zero. It's a tremendous hindrance. People have been brought up with death through heart attacks and strokes almost as part of their Wheaties in the morning. It's expected that Uncle Fred will die of a heart attack; it's part and parcel of our Western experience. Time and time again, even in this day and age, I see patients who express surprise that smoking is dangerous, express surprise that inappropriate diets are bad, express surprise that blood pressure affects the heart.

I suppose that it's not until fairly recently that the importance of primary prevention has been recognized. But unless patients come through systems such as companies taking out private insurance for their employees, where everyone goes off and has a BUPA screen once a year, which I certainly would recommend, that is about the only way you will pick up a lot of the people who are just sitting around waiting for their arteries to block off and die in the middle of the night.

We now have things such as balloons, which we actually insert indirectly via a puncture in the artery in the leg or arm, up into the heart, and manipulate the size and quality of the artery, replacing direct surgical inspection. That's a terrifically exciting thing to be able to do, and the effects on patients are absolutely profound: you see a patient come in with crippling chest pain, who would otherwise have been sent to a surgeon, and then within a day be able to send him out having repaired his artery in under an hour, with local anaesthesia – it's just a phenomenal advance.

If you get to hospital in time, even if you've had your first heart attack, you've got an 80 per cent chance of having it reverted with specific drugs targeted at the acute event. A heart attack is due to the closure of an artery resulting from a clot, and we can now administer an agent which will dissolve the clot. If we get to the patient in under an hour, virtually all patients will go back to a normal heart muscle function. They might be left with a narrowing artery, but we can then put a balloon across it, so that one can actually very easily return the heart to a structurally normal organ, whereas ten years ago you would have been looking at a widow-making event. This is used to such an extent in America that many cities with expertise in cardiovascular treatment are experiencing a population boom in the areas around such hospitals, and it's suddenly hit home that instead of saying heart attack is part and parcel of life, this no longer needs to be the case. That's why the situation where you've got only sixty full-time cardiologists in this country is so disgraceful.

We've got a guy on the ward who came in yesterday about to die. He had E C G electrical signals which showed major occlusion of the arteries. Horrible. I mean, I thought this guy was on his way out of here. We gave him the drug, ten minutes later he's back to normal. He'll be home on Saturday. But that happens infrequently now, and the reason is not only because we get to the patients way too late but because their own awareness of heart disease is very low.

Patients usually stay at home. 'I've got indigestion,' they say, and one of the reasons they do that is psychological. It's much better to have a problem below the diaphragm than above it. Doctors, particularly GPs, if they're called up one evening by a patient complaining of pain in the lower part of the chest, will almost certainly just by reflex action say, 'It's probably your ulcer playing up.' Having an ulcer's no big deal and it's not going to kill you. But heart disease – well, that *is* going to kill you, and people don't want to know about the potential implications, so on first presentation, patients will be dissuaded both by their own psychology and the psychology of their doctor from assuming a heart problem.

But the first glimmer a patient has that he might have heart disease terrifies him, pain from the heart is a peculiarly terrifying experience. One of the hallmarks of having a heart attack is the sheer terror of the experience, related only in part to the severity of the pain. There's something awful about the premonition of death which patients experience, and once they've experienced that, it's often not difficult to convince them of the need to give up smoking or change their diet. But try and get the same message through to the patient who thinks he's well: 'Oh, it can't happen to me.'

There's another problem. We all think we're too busy to take exercise. 'Life is hectic enough', is the often said excuse, 'without having to get up an hour earlier to take exercise.' And food is another problem. I mean, just take our hospitals! If you walk around a hospital and see what patients get for breakfast, it's a boiled egg and white bread with butter: heavily cholesterol-containing food, no nutritious intake in terms of protein and folic acid and iron and all that stuff, all bleached out with the white bread, and butter, which we ought to be discouraging. It makes you weep.

But, you see, the problem is that if you increase the level of awareness, if you open that floodgate, you can imagine the numbers of customers who are going to come through the NHS public door, and we simply don't have the beds available. Hospitals are closing beds. And then, ten beds out of 200 this year are for AIDS patients. Next year, sixty beds out of 200 might be for AIDS patients. Of course, they ought to make it sixty beds out of 260 – but the figure is likely to remain 200, so beds are eroding all the time. So what's going to happen to the patients with cancer and heart disease squeezed out by the AIDS epidemic? Where should the priorities be assigned? Should they be assigned to patients who have got retrievable, reversible, treatable coronary cause, in a population which makes positive contributions to the community? Or should they be targeted at the derelict intravenous drug abuser? I mean, it's a major question. And where have resources been targeted? They've been targeted at the derelict, intravenous drug abuser and the gay population, because that's the population mainly at risk now. I'm not saying we shouldn't treat them, but the grim reality is that as a result of the loss of beds, those who suffer will be the patients that I could cure.

American practice in cardiology is developed to the extent that people will take medico-legal action against an authority, a hospital, a doctor, that doesn't offer them treatment for reversal of a heart attack. It's seen as a neglect of a hospital's duty not to have such treatment offered. And when you see someone come through the door here with a potentially reversible heart attack who hasn't been able to get to proper medical services, one can't but wonder whether he wouldn't have a case against us. Another point: we have a six- to eight-month waiting list for important valvular or vascular surgery. Four patients in the last six months have died on my waiting list, one of them a forty-eight-year-old with three small children. It's disgraceful. Those patients should never have to wait. If I lived in America, I'd probably be sued. And I couldn't easily defend it.

DR BRIAN GAZZARD
AIDS SPECIALIST

═══════

I WAS, to be honest, getting a bit bored, and I was looking for a new outlet, and along came AIDS, and AIDS is the most fascinating thing; I mean, it's right back medically to the nineteenth century when tuberculosis was being described, you know, all clinical description, and a whole host of new conditions that hadn't been seen before and for which there was no effective treatment. Of course, that's what doctors like to do most: they like to see new diseases – and I've seen so many new diseases that other people haven't seen, or have been seen unbelievably rarely, it's just fascinating. And the group of patients involved are interesting and have got different views on life, and different sexual *mores* that are very interesting, and it's just a fascinating area.

I saw the first patient in this country with AIDS in 1981. He came in with what was thought to be a venereal disease, and had a whole series of tests, none of which were ever diagnosable as anything. He said he was a monogamous homosexual; of course, he turned out not to be monogamous, he turned out to have lots of partners, and his partners came along and I got interested in them – so the whole thing snowballed from there.

My senior registrar at the time had gone off to San Francisco on holiday, and as he was rather broke, he stayed in the homosexual quarter with his wife and three kids, and he wrote to me and said, 'There's a new disease sweeping the States called AIDS.' And the very next day, it's fantastically serendipitous really, the first reports appeared in the medical journals of these unusual chest x-rays of pneumocystic pneumonia, and that week, my first patient reappeared with the same chest x-ray. In fact the radiologist said to me, 'Isn't this pneumocystic pneumonia?' And I said, 'Yes, gosh it is, I've just looked at the papers,' and so we diagnosed it, and that's how it all started.

So we knew that he had AIDS, and he lived for a couple of years and then he died. We had a very interesting post-mortem in which we saw a very rare tumour of the brain called a microglioma. It's a well-recognized AIDS phenomenon; it's a tumour of the lymph system of the brain, and has become a common tumour in AIDS, although unbelievably rare in the general context of medicine.

I'm still a gastroenterologist. Most gastroenterologists are also general physicians. I mean, for example, I'm on take twice a week, I see strokes, I see meningitis, I see pneumonia and deal with it all. And I feel very, very strongly that somebody with a very broad training has got to deal with AIDS, because there are neurological problems, there are rheumatological problems, there are gastroenterological problems, there are chest problems, and so somebody who's got some experience with all of them has to be in charge somewhere and hold the reins and parcel out the difficult problems to colleagues, and really gastroenterology is one of the few specialties left which does impinge upon so many other specialties.

Before patients develop AIDS, they become ill non-specifically, with abnormality of the tongue called hereoluplakia, fungus infections of the mouth called candida, they feel tired and can't work, they sweat at night, they have diarrhoea. That's called ARC or AIDS Related Complex. If you've got ARC, you're going to get AIDS within a year or so, and then be dead in two years, so it's a fairly late stage of the disease.

After ARC they go on and get what we call full-blown AIDS. By that we mean infections which you or I wouldn't get, because although we are exposed to these organisms all the time, we don't get ill with them because we've got an intact immune system, whereas an AIDS patient has no immune responses, their immune system has collapsed. And the commonest opportunistic infection is pneumocystic pneumonia, which causes pneumonia of the lungs. The second commonest probably is a diarrhoeal illness called cryptosporidial diarrhoea, which you or I might get as a brief traveller's diarrhoea, but goes on for months in AIDS patients and is a devastating illness. There's toxoplasma, which in normal people produces a bit of lymph nodes and a bit of fever for a week or two, and they can get better and never get it again, but in AIDS patients they get a big brain abscess and may die of it. Then there's an infection called cytomegalovirus infection, which causes blindness, fevers and a whole host of symptoms in AIDS patients. And there's a very unusual meningitis called cryptococcheal meningitis, which is a fungus infection of the brain, which again is very common in AIDS patients, and there is a very odd tumour, a vascular tumour called Kaposi's sarcoma, which is a purplish black raised nodule on the skin, a highly malignant tumour, which eventually they would die of.

AIDS patients have such an unpleasant time in that month coming up to death, both psychologically and physically, that they're often glad to be released from it at that point in their lives.

Like any fatal disease in a young group of people, there's tremendous anxiety; they go through a period of depression, a period of aggression – you know, society has somehow done something to them; and then of reluctant acceptance of the inevitable. There's clearly a strong stigma attached to AIDS in this country, and so it's difficult to talk to their friends and their relatives about their condition, and that makes it much worse. Everybody feels sorry for you if you've got, say, a tumour of the testis. You can talk about it, and get a lot of support that way. But with AIDS, the sad thing is that a lot of people blame you: I've heard people say, 'Well, it's their own bloody fault anyway.' So the whole situation is very difficult.

As 98 per cent of the patients in the AIDS ward are homosexuals, there's a different ambiance. I mean, there are occasional drag shows, and, you know, entertainments of that sort, but I think it's like any ward where a high proportion of the patients are dying. I think the kind of courage displayed by human beings at times of stress is often remarkable, and you gain strength from that. And I think that one's got a great deal of insight into what pleasant, thoughtful, caring people they are, but I suppose one should have known that before. It's the one ward I know in London where there's a waiting list for nurses to try and work there.

The general public still knows amazingly little about AIDS. The depressing statistics after the public health campaign is that 40 per cent of the population still think that you actually get AIDS by giving blood or by kissing and that sort of thing.

First of all, it's very difficult to catch, rather than easy to catch. Secondly, it is caught sexually, and therefore it's really all related to promiscuity. The fact is that you're only susceptible if you are having promiscuous sex. Thirdly, the epidemic could be stopped in its tracks if two things were done: one, if condoms were always worn, both homosexually and heterosexually, and two, if homosexuals gave up anal receptive intercourse – they could do almost anything else. You see, in the spread of the AIDS virus, we believe that you require the virus or lymphocytes containing the virus to come in direct contact with blood; so, for example, if you cut yourself and I cut myself and we mingle our blood intimately, then you might get the virus. Now obviously that doesn't happen very often, whereas what happens in anal intercourse is that semen is deposited in the rectum, and there's lots of virus in the semen, and with the rectum often damaged during intercourse, torn or bleeding, it's a perfect breeding ground. Anal intercourse is a traumatic process; the anus was not designed as a sexual passage.

At the moment there's an exponential growth rate only in defined groups: in homosexuals, in drug addicts and in heterosexuals in Africa. What we need to know here is, will there be an epidemic amongst heterosexuals? Now, clearly there will never be an epidemic amongst monogamous heterosexuals, safely married, only one partner for life. They are for ever protected, and so it's really a question of whether there will be an epidemic in promiscuous young people, so that they won't grow old and become monogamous, or whether they will become infected before they become monogamous, and then infect their partner and their offspring – and then we would really have a devastating global problem on our hands.

There is no sign that there's an epidemic in heterosexuals, but the problem really is, you wouldn't necessarily be able to see whether an epidemic was starting, because we have no policy of public testing.

I have very mixed views about testing in terms of confidentiality and personal rights: there is a difficult judgement between what is personal liberty, and a right to total confidentiality, versus a public health need to know whether an epidemic is occurring, to know which groups are infected and therefore to advise them the best possible way to avoid affecting other people.

One of the problems about AIDS is that there are relatively few people who know a lot about AIDS in the medical sense and who are qualified to speak about the ethics of the problem. I haven't suddenly become an expert on ethics, I haven't suddenly been given extra insight into whether or not testing on a wide scale should be performed, and my views about ethics are no more important than anybody else's in the general public; all I know is a great deal about the medical aspects of AIDS.

Well, homosexuals have a whole subculture, and a set of views about life which are different: sex and love are much more divorced in that situation than they are heterosexually; sex is very unrelated to love really, it's a form of release which is readily available on a wide scale. And so they can have a highly promiscuous sexual life and still sometimes form a really close relationship at another level, and they successfully manage to divorce those two issues, and up to the advent of AIDS, in a way with no problem. Any illness they might contract was treatable. In fact, the vast majority of people who have AIDS were infected at the stage where they wouldn't have known what they were doing would result in AIDS.

I pricked myself with an HIV-positive needle a few years ago now, and that was a very traumatic experience because that was early on; we didn't know what the risks of getting it were. And of course they're very slight fortunately. I know now that I'm not positive, but I went through an extremely stressed period not knowing whether I was positive or not, knowing that sexual relationships with my wife would be potentially dangerous, and I had a very difficult time and found it very difficult to settle into anything. It's quite interesting how you work harder and keep busy because you don't want to stop and think. So I had a lot of insight into what it must be like for patients waiting for the results, and I had to wait a long time, one has got to wait three to six months to see whether the virus will grow in your body. I can remember it very clearly, that will never leave me. I pricked myself, and I looked at the blood on my finger and thought, 'Shit, I'm always doing that . . . oh my God, that patient's positive!' I mean, it suddenly struck me what I'd done to myself. I can see the room where I actually did it and I can see the blood welling up in my finger, and it's interesting actually, the finger where I did it, I mean, I still will feel it rather rough, and I think, 'God, that's where it happened.' That was a fairly profound experience for me.

One of the things I often say is that a serious medical illness is a great way of making you realize what is important or unimportant in your life. You suddenly realize that you put the daffodils in, and it's terribly important to see them growing next year, and you get a great deal of joy out of all that. You're so busy usually in the routine of humdrum life, living for the future rather than for the present; the whole of society thinks too much about saving money, working too hard because they're going to enjoy themselves in ten years, rather than enjoy themselves now. It's terribly important to enjoy yourself each day.

It's impossible to answer how much we know about AIDS.

There is more money being spent on AIDS, and there are more bright people working in AIDS, than virtually any other field of medicine. The virus was discovered in 1983, and we know more about that virus than any other virus that's been discovered in the last thirty years. That's an amazing tribute to science, actually. It shows if you really do spend enough money, you get amazing results. It's unbelievably lucky that it didn't occur ten years earlier, because both virology and immunology were so poorly advanced we would have made no impact on the disease at all.

As a group, AIDS doctors are very involved in the political process because of its very high political profile, and the recognition that the epidemic will be here in the future, and the need to make plans. The trouble with all politicians – I don't mean this rudely – is the rather short term on which they operate. I mean, perhaps only two or three years for the Minister of Health. And with an epidemic of this sort, you need very long-term planning, you need to look into the 1990s and the year 2000 to be prepared. And I know most politicians have got so many problems from day to day that to look into the future is very difficult.

But 50 per cent of homosexuals in London are now positive in HIV virus, and my belief is that most of those people will get AIDS unless some treatment comes along. And so the figures are clearly bound to be enormous, and the numbers that we're seeing now are going to be dwarfed by the numbers we will see by 1995 in the homosexual population.

And what we don't know is whether heterosexuals, as a group, will get the disease. If they do, the impact is absolutely catastrophic to the National Health Service; if there's an epidemic in heterosexuals, then clearly the whole face of the National Health Service is going to radically alter.

I would put it 40 to 60 against it happening. A lot of people would put it 70 to 30 in favour of it happening, but I'm an optimist in that I think that the majority of people are not particularly promiscuous. The fact that 4 million condoms are being sold each week now, the straws in the wind are rather encouraging.

DR WILLIE HARRIS

VENEREOLOGIST

I was born in Northern Ireland and I lived and went to school in Ballymena, County Antrim. I was very keen to be a doctor from my days at grammar school. I remember fracturing my leg, in fact I had two fractures in two subsequent years, and I was therefore in hospital both times, and the care and concern of the doctors made a lasting impression upon me. And I suppose also in a community such as that the medical practitioners have a very high social status level. In Ireland there are the clergy, the doctors and the veterinary surgeons.

When I qualified I knew that I wanted to do some branch of hospital medicine, but I wasn't sure what I wanted to do particularly. I was the only student who had done an elective in venereology, and I remember thinking to myself afterwards that I would never again want to do *that*. It just so happened that one of the two consultants in venereology in Northern Ireland (there were only two) had died – he had a heart attack. And because I was the only student who had ever done it, the remaining consultant actually got in touch with me and asked, 'Look, would you be able to help us out?'

So there was a special job made for me, which is a most unusual event to have occurred. But I suppose the things that happen in life are frequently directed by fortune. At that time venereology was not a field which was attracting people who would be regarded as having good potential academic careers – it was a field which was looked upon as rather backwater medicine – and there had been relatively little research going on in it for a number of years. With the discovery of penicillin, there was a tremendous drop in syphilis and gonorrhoea after the Second World War, the American public health service had closed down many of its clinics and teaching hospitals, and in the United Kingdom, there was a reduction in the number of specialist units in venereology. Altogether the service was not seen as a prestige specialty, nor as an area of future development of medicine.

At that time, not just in Northern Ireland but in all parts of the country, I would have thought there was a good deal of shame attached to having venereal diseases. The units which existed in the teaching hospitals at that time were usually in basements, or far away from the rest of the other outpatients. Patients were seen in a fairly cloak and dagger atmosphere; there was this feeling of importance of maintaining anonymity and keeping the thing very quiet. This stigma was not only among the patients, funnily enough; the nursing staff and the doctors working in the specialty were thought to be just slightly different, but that, thank goodness, has changed a lot.

The field has changed enormously; the calibre of the new entrants we now have in the field is far superior to the people we took in ten or twelve years ago. When you have difficult diagnostic problems then you will always attract and interest young, capable staff, and once you start to get one or two good people in, then you attract more. In medicine, the prestige of a field is frequently related to the difficulty of the problems that it faces. Anything that you can do easily and well, where all your patients live and everything is wonderful, nobody who is young or ambitious or has an active mind that wants challenges will be attracted to that field. If you look back at the beginning of this century, the people who treated syphilis were among the top physicians of the day.

Our work has changed an awful lot in the last few years with AIDS in the sense that previously most of the people I saw I could cure. Now it is fair to say that a lot of the patients I see have infections that I can't cure, we can only alleviate. And not just AIDS: the viral conditions generally, particularly papilloma virus, which is related to cervical cancer.

You haven't heard much about papilloma virus. That's really because AIDS and HIV have taken over the stage, but in fact the most rapidly increasing sexually transmitted disease in the UK at the moment is papilloma virus. It's a wart virus infection, just like the warts you get on your hand, only a different type which are related to premalignant change in the female cervix. PV infects both sexes, but the long-term and severe effects are on the female.

I would say that one of the problems with venereology is that the infections you are seeing are just a symptom of behaviour patterns. If you can't alter the behaviour patterns in society, then you will just keep on treating the symptom, and treating patients on an individual basis actually changes nothing in the long run.

To give you an example. As you know, there is a good correlation between cigarette smoking and premature death. Yet for many years doctors have slogged away looking after those patients whose health was ruined by smoking, when you could argue that it would have been much more worthwhile to concentrate on trying to cut down the sale of cigarettes.

When I was a child I was attracted to medicine initially because the doctor seemed to be someone who was very important in society, and was doing work that no one else wanted to do, and this seemed to be a wonderful thing. But I don't look on myself as doing anything wonderful, or being wonderful because I am a doctor. I just see myself as someone who takes care of people, who takes responsibility and trains people, and who is very lucky to be doing the sort of job that I am doing, because venereology suits my personality very well. I enjoy the patient contact; I enjoy understanding people or trying to understand them; I enjoy taking histories and trying to do the detective work, sorting out their contacts; I enjoy making diagnoses; and I enjoy getting them better and supporting them, even if they are not going to get better. So it is a lovely job.

But it is very hard work. There is continuous outpatient work;

nine or ten hours a day of interviewing and examining people day after day after day in never-ending numbers is very stressful.

I don't see how our society can really afford to effectively recompense people like myself in relation to the service that we provide. There's no question about it. I mean, we work hard and way beyond our contract hours because we want to – so that's our choice. But it's sad that we're not better paid; we'd certainly be a lot better paid in North America. But I mean, we're here, and there's a monopoly employer, so I don't see the situation changing.

SISTER SUE HINDLE
NURSE (PRIVATE)

═══════

WELL, I come from a medical family; my father's a GP and my mother's a nurse, so it's the natural progression. The practice was in the house and we answered the phone from when we were very small; I wanted to nurse at the age of five, and I never wanted to do anything else, ever.

When I got to UCH, it was my first time in London. It's very different from being a non-medical student. There wasn't any sort of freshers' week, or any organized social life, and if you weren't very careful you could end up really quite lonely. I didn't know anybody and it took quite a while to actually become established, and for all that everybody says about being a student, that certainly wasn't the happiest of times. The nurses' residence off Tottenham Court Road was a revolting place to live. It was built around a well, so that everybody looked into everybody else's room, and you couldn't see the weather without actually hanging your head out the window and looking upwards, so that was all a bit grotty.

I'd led quite a secluded life really; I'd been very protected by the parents, the same school from the age of dot to the age of eighteen, and so to leave home and to have to survive was quite amazing. My mother used to send food parcels to start off with because it just never entered my head to go shopping, and I lost a stone when I first started because I was unhappy, and I just hadn't worked out how to do things. And then gradually you find friends and you work out how to do it.

After qualification, I worked in casualty for just over eighteen months and that was amazing really. I had a marvellous time. You didn't know what would be next, it was very exciting. After that I went on a surgical ward just to get experience, then I got a sister's job at St Mary's, in ITU (Intensive Therapy Unit), and I just left there last August and moved into the private sector.

I went because I was very unhappy with the fact that things were so desperate within the National Health Service. The care that we were giving was appalling, *I* couldn't do anything about it, and I had bashed my head against the wall for so long.

When I left there was a mixture of envy, because I'm being paid more than they are, and horror – you know, the phrase that was bantered about at Mary's: 'The rat leaving the sinking ship'. The thing is, most of the people I know would come over immediately if the jobs they wanted were available.

I still have loyalty to the NHS. I'm very sad to have gone, partly because they taught me everything that I know and partly because the nature of what we do in the NHS is charitable, if you like, and a large element of me enjoys doing nursing for next to nothing, and I don't like being mercenary about it. But part of me thinks, 'Well, God damn it, I've done it for long enough for next to nothing and I'm not a charity', and there comes a point where, you know, at twenty-eight, I think it's about time I could afford a flat.

It's a small hospital – well, I say it's small because I compare it to the NHS, but by British private standards, it's sort of moderate size, it's got 120 beds. It's one of the most profitable hospitals in the country; it's owned by AMI, American Medical . . . I can't remember. It's modern, and I think it's very nice.

The private sector is just a million miles away from the National Health Service. Well, it's a business, so it has to make a profit, and everybody has to be a part of that, because if they're not, then it won't. And it has to function efficiently. And that doesn't apply in the National Health Service. You don't have to be efficient, you don't have to do anything provided you arrive at work every day.

In the NHS you'd often have time to waste. Well, you don't have that in the private sector because anybody who's not needed is sent home, and you employ your staff on the ratio to your patients. Each day I calculate how much help I think I need, and that's put into the computer and it decides how many nurses I need. We run on a small skeleton staff, and there's a big bank of staff who are flexible and work when we ask them to. So for instance, if there are no patients over Christmas, there will be less staff.

When I first arrived everybody was full of smiles, and welcoming, which in actual fact is because they enjoy the place, and also I think because it's American. They all learnt my name straight away and everybody said, 'Hello, Sue, it's nice that you're here.' There are lots of training sessions and a lot of indoctrination, and there's a thing called Team Briefing from somewhere at head office in America.

I've been away on two courses recently. One was to teach me how to be a better manager of the people that I've got in order to conserve the amount of people that I use, and thereby save more money. And 'Customer Services' was the other one. That's making sure that you're pleasant to people, and understand that while the customer is not necessarily right, you have to accept his perception of things, because whether it's right or wrong, that is his perception. And I would never have gone on anything like that in the National Health Service.

I wondered whether it would all be very cold and calculating – just simply get them in and out, and take the money – and it's not. In fact I was quite impressed by that. Nurses are nurses and they still care enormously. I'm very proud of my nurses.

The one thing that I've really noticed is that I'm actually pleasant to people now, whereas I'd got to the stage in the NHS where I really wasn't as pleasant to the patients as I should have been. I wasn't nasty, but I certainly wouldn't go out of my way to be nice to anybody, because I was so fed up and sick to the back teeth of everything, and I couldn't do anything about anything anyway. And I'm not like that at all now. I'm much more confident as well, because they respect me and they value what I say. Right from the top, even the director of the hospital knows who I am, whereas the director of nursing at St Mary's, when I left, having been there for two years as one of their sisters, didn't know who I was. And that grinds you down. You think, if she doesn't know who I am, then she just can't be running the place as she should be.

Because the patients are paying, they think that they deserve something better than they would have got in the National Health, where they weren't paying – in fact they were paying, but there you go. And whereas the National Health patients generally speaking were very, very grateful for everything that you did – you know, if they saw you once a day, they'd be thrilled to bits that they'd actually set eyes on you – in the private sector they go bananas if they haven't seen you for the past three minutes.

I love talking to the patients, and I love listening to them; it's fascinating, because they're so different. You know, they own this and that, they are wealthy people. Not that that makes them more interesting, but sometimes they've done more interesting things as a result of that, so they're just different from Mrs Joe Bloggs who is lovely in herself but may not have done such exciting things. I was talking to a lady yesterday about holidays; she was looking through some brochures and she said she couldn't find anywhere to go because they'd been everywhere!

AMI demands more of me than the National Health did, and expects me to give my all to them, and I do an awful lot of overtime – for which I get paid – so I tend to be there an awful lot. Plus, there are a lot of social gatherings that I'm expected to be at, and weekends away, the courses and things.

I've just been on the IER course, which is Involvement, Excellence and Results, and that's very American. I've got this huge file in the car of the things that I'm supposed to learn, and there are more courses in the future. We're going on a . . . what do you call it? You know, when you rush off to the Welsh mountains and jump into rivers and things, a sort of orienteering type thing for team building . . . It sounds brilliant to me.

I'm more confident in me now, I feel like I am capable of something. Before this, I'd got to the stage where I thought I was capable of nothing. Despite the fact that I could run an intensive care unit, I used to think, I can't be worth very much, nobody was interested in my opinions or my views on anything. So it's certainly made me think about me, and about what I'm capable of and what I can achieve.

I don't know whether I'd have ever bought the flat. The money difference wasn't sufficient to have made the difference, but it was something that I'd ummed and ahhed about for ages and ages, and it's a huge mortgage, but I've done it now, and I suspect that's as a result of the move.

DR JOHN HUNTER

GASTROENTEROLOGIST

GASTROENTEROLOGY is the study of diseases of the stomach and the intestine. It includes the bowels and liver, pancreas, gall bladder, all that sort of thing. Basically, it starts at the mouth and ends at the anus.

By and large I see cases which have gastrointestinal disorders: liver disease, ulcers, colitis; we have people with difficulty swallowing, strictures, narrowing of the oesophagus, oesophagitis caused by perhaps a reflux of acid up from the stomach into the gullet through a hiatus hernia. In the stomach we might have gastritis caused by drugs or infection, we might have ulcers, we might have cancer. Then there's disease of the duodenum. You have patients with carcinoma of the pancreas or bile ducts; they might have gall stones, they might have liver disease. Liver disease is a considerable percentage of my work. Patients by and large drink too much and they get cirrhosis; cirrhosis leads to various complications like swollen blood vessels in the oesophagus and stomach which may bleed: that leads to jaundice, swelling of the belly, ascites, dropsy and fluid in the abdominal cavity – there's a whole area of work related to the liver. Then there's the small intestine, which is primarily involved with the absorption of nutrients from the diet, and diseases affecting that may cause malnutrition. There's the large intestine, where you get colitis and tumours of the bowel. And finally, you have the anus, where there are various conditions like piles and fissures.

So it's quite a wide range. In fact, gastroenterology, in terms of the number of cases, is one of the most important specialties. If

you look at the number of admissions to hospital, I think gastroenterology overall, including things like appendicitis and ulcers
and everything, accounts for more than any other single specialty.

The great thing about gastroenterology is that there's an enormous lot of good you can do to your patients. I mean, there are
some specialties, like neurology for instance, where by and large
the specialist role is diagnostic; they'll say, 'Well, you've got this
condition,' say, multiple sclerosis, and at the moment there's very
little one can offer the patient in the way of treatment that's
going to make a great deal of difference. I mean, most cases of
multiple sclerosis gradually get worse. Gastroenterology is totally
different; obviously we see some patients with advanced cancer
where we can do nothing, but with the majority of our patients,
we can get them better.

I do hundreds of endoscopic examinations of the gut, and
these endoscopes are marvels of modern technology. You can
pass them into the colon, all the way along, and you can see the
whole large bowel as clearly as if you were looking at the back of
your hand. It's a sort of pink colour, and there are blood vessels
running everywhere, like the branches of a tree spreading out in
every direction, and then you pass another bend and you're not
quite sure what you'll find there – I think that's incredibly
beautiful and exciting. It takes a lot of skill to manoeuvre an
endoscope around the colon, it makes you a little bit of a surgeon,
but it's a very satisfying technique to be able to do, and very
valuable; you detect all sorts of diseases at a much earlier stage.

I never get bored with doing endoscopy and looking around
the human body. There's no doubt that the actual finer structure
of the body is really such a marvel: it is just incredible how this
extremely complex structure should have arisen, and that it's so
efficient by and large and that it functions so well most of the
time. The average layman, if he saw a naked lady, he wouldn't
think that was ugly, he would think that was rather beautiful.
And to my way of thinking, the structure of the muscles and the
nerves underneath are, when they're healthy, just as beautiful.
Diseased organs don't look nice, something best avoided. The

other thing, of course: whatever colour the patient's skin, inside the rectum they all look identical – which is a very instructive thought.

The least enjoyable bits about the job are, in a word, shit. Because a lot of my patients have bowel disorders, so you have to do examinations of their rectum, and I don't think anyone really takes a liking for faeces. And sometimes they may be passing lots of blood in their stools, or fat, they may pass black stools or white stools, or red stools. There's a general aversion to faeces even amongst the medical profession because it's horrible, unpleasant stuff to work with. Urine is bad enough. Most people like to work with blood because blood is nice and clean and you can centrifuge it and measure various chemicals in it . . . marvellous. But the study of faeces is nothing like as advanced as the study of blood. Very few patients like collecting their faeces; we are trained from a very early age to get rid of it cleanly and decently, not to play with it, and this sort of indoctrination lasts for the rest of our lives.

Well, I wouldn't want you to think that this is a big hang-up, it's just that if you go to a patient who is perhaps bleeding from an ulcer, and he has been incontinent in the bed passing what we call melaena stools, which are black, tarry faeces which has only partly digested blood from higher up in the digestive tract, quite honestly there's a horrible stink, it's messy, dirty, gets everywhere, it's difficult to clean, and also it may convey infection.

Furthermore, it is extremely complex. What happens is that the food is eaten, it's digested, and most of the contents of the food that is of value to the body is absorbed from the small intestine. What goes into the large intestine is waste, which will be stuff like bran and fibres from meat, fruit, vegetables, which are acted on by all the bacteria that live there. These ferment it and break it down, and in breaking it down, they themselves grow and reproduce, and the actual faeces then is a combination of the bacteria, the remnants of the food, plus a few cells and things that have been shed from the centre of the gut through which the contents flow. The bacteria breaking down all these various chemicals result in the production of so many other compounds that the actual chemistry involved is extremely complicated.

I'm always absolutely open with my patients. I tell them everything that they ask me. I try and judge what they want me to tell them so that I won't burden someone with knowledge that they've got cancer if I don't think they want to know it. I will tell patients exactly what's happening in so far as they are capable of understanding it. And a lot of people are very intelligent and very knowledgeable and I'll have a discussion with them almost as fully as I might with another doctor. And I feel that there's no way that one should pretend that it's all magic they can't understand. And that's as it should be, because in the end every man is responsible for his own health; I'm only advising them.

I'm very much surrounded by death. However beautiful I may have said the body is, the doctor is working with imperfect clay. I may make a brilliant diagnosis and get a patient better, but a few years later the patients will have some other problem. It's not as if I can be like an architect and built St Paul's Cathedral and it will be standing for years with everyone admiring it. I know that at the end of the day I've got to fail, that any patient, however well I may heal their ulcer or get rid of their irritable bowel, something else will turn up and eventually that patient will die. Even though I live with that knowledge, none the less, whenever they do actually die it's always distressing.

I had a patient die right in front of me last Sunday afternoon. This patient was bleeding very vigorously from the gasrointestinal tract, and I was attempting to pass a tube to stop the bleeding. The patient was extremely anaemic, we were pouring blood into a vein, and what happened was that whilst I was trying to put this tube down his throat, he vomited blood and inhaled some of it into his lungs, and although we sucked it all out, he had a respiratory arrest and then a cardiac arrest. He was an old man, nearly eighty, and he wasn't very fit, he had been cirrhotic for years, and he just couldn't take this insult, and he died. So there was not only the sadness at the death of a man I'd known for the last two or three years – and your patients tend to become almost friends – but also the fact that I failed in what I set out to do, which was to save his life. So even after twenty years, death is never taken lightly.

The actual process of death itself is very banal. I mean, he just stopped breathing and then his heart stopped. He went blue. We worked like fury trying to resuscitate him but it didn't work. There was nothing terribly dramatic about that, it was just a technical business. But it's afterwards, when you realize that you've failed, and he's dead, that you have the emotional reaction. Obviously you try and suppress that. I had to go home and take my family out for dinner that evening, and I was trying to be a pleasant father, but it was difficult to be a pleasant father when I'd just lost the battle over this particular patient.

I can't say that I am religious. I was brought up in a very strong Church of England family, and until the age of about twenty I used to be a regular attender. But I was then seized with great doubts, which have lasted ever since. I would say that I was agnostic at the moment. I cannot honestly see how a mechanism as complex as the human body actually arises by simple evolution from primeval slime matter; I mean, it is incredible that chance should derive such a complex structure. Whether that means that there's a God, I really don't know; I mean, if you look at the way the world goes on, to believe in a God and an afterlife seems incredible really.

Well, we're making incredible progress in medicine really; the advance of technology is astounding. I mean, when I was a medical student, if you talked about transplantation, my lecturers would say, 'We'll never get them.' And now it's routine, people are living for years with hearts and kidneys transplanted.

And in my own field we're starting to study the wall of the colon, which I believe we shall find is very important in limiting the number of diseases. The large intestine, which is called the colon in strict anatomical terms, goes around to the rectum and anus and is full of bacteria. Really we know so little about the effects of these bacteria – millions and millions of them, every gramme of faeces has something like 75 million bacteria, and we know as little about that as we know about the brain. But in 100 years time we shall be automatically controlling the bacteria that live in the gut, so that when a baby's born, we shall look at the child's genetic make-up and say, 'This child needs certain bacteria to have optimum health', and we shall be getting that genetic make-up by amniocentesis before the child is born; we shall immediately give him the right bacteria, and this will cut down on a massive number of intestinal diseases such as celiac disease, eczema, asthma, things like that, and I think that this will improve human health enormously.

I'm interested in disorders of the gut, particularly what's called inflammatory bowel disease, which is colitis in its various forms, and this accounts for 50 per cent of all the consultations done by British gastroenterologists. We think that certain bacteria in the bowel may possibly be causing this trouble by metabolizing food residues to produce chemicals which cause the bowel upset, and my main research interest at the moment is the affect that specific foods can have in provoking gastrointestinal disease and symptoms. It's an interesting condition in that these patients have symptoms like diarrhoea and constipation, pain in the belly, bloating, wind, and yet when you examine them, despite all our modern technology, you cannot find anything wrong with them.

This will be my research interest for the next four or five years. At the end of that time, either I shall prove that it is important, in which case money will be much easier to get, and if I am wrong – I don't think I am because virtually everything I do confirms to me my belief that we're on the right track – but at the end of the day, if I am wrong, at least that's a cul de sac that some other people won't have to go down.

I was always so interested in medicine and research that I could never really countenance any other career. But I gave up quite a lot to do that; I think your family lose out in the sense that you work so hard. O K, they've got more money to spend, but I think that I've spent less time with my family than I would have wished to do, and it's probably made me a much narrower person. For instance, I don't read as much as I'd like to; when I was a student I used to write a lot for student magazines and things like that, and all I've written since I've qualified is medical papers. Sometimes I think of novels that I would like to write. Well, perhaps I'll write them when I'm retired. It's a very demanding career. But medicine's been so fascinating that overall I prefer to give up the other things.

Our research team comprises a research doctor who's nearly at the end of his tenure; I've got two research dieticians, one of whom is part-time, one full-time; I've got a research biochemist and a research nurse who also acts as the secretary. There's also another research technician shortly to be appointed. And *we* have to generate all the funds to pay them, they're not paid for by the NHS, and we have to get various research grants, which is very difficult in the present climate.

But our patients do sponsored cycle rides, they knit and they make jam and things like that. One lady is making tea towels and selling them, and some of our wealthier patients have made very large donations. One man went swimming on Christmas Day, and raised £2,000, which was an incredible performance. But I'm sorry that we have to do all this to raise money; it's a terrible waste of my time. For instance, there's a golf club down the road that's having a social day for us next month, and we've got to send a team along and shake hands and talk to people and collect a cheque at the end of the day. Now, don't get me wrong, I think these people who are giving up their time and working for us are marvellous. It's just that the people who are actually doing the research shouldn't have to be raising the money, and time you give to raising money is time you could have been spending doing the research, or with your family.

So it's far from ideal, but it has meant that it's possible for us to go ahead with the next phase of our research. And if I'm not enthusiastic and I don't follow it up, no one else will. And I do feel really that I've gained an awful lot from medicine, and I have to put something back in.

PROFESSOR MALCOLM JAYSON

RHEUMATOLOGIST

My father is an accountant – he's over eighty and still practising – two brothers are accountants, my uncle's an accountant, so are my cousins – everyone's an accountant in the family, except me!

When I was a junior doctor I wanted something which did not have the very acute emergency on-call, so I could study in the evenings. And I found that I liked the type of medicine which involved getting to know people – and this is a specialty where you do need to get to know people. I found I enjoyed that more than the acute, middle of the night heroics, you know, dealing with a bleeding ulcer and once you've dealt with it, the patient goes on his way and that's the end of it. I like talking to people, getting to know them as people. I think you've got to be a nice person to be a rheumatologist, and you can't be a good rheumatologist if you're not interested in people.

Well, there are about 200 different sorts of arthritis, of which the most common are the wear and tear types which affect something like 80–90 per cent of the population over a lifetime, although most of them are relatively trivial; rheumatoid arthritis affects about 2 or 3 per cent of the female population and 1–2 per cent of the male population, so it is less common but potentially much more severe and crippling. Some forms of arthritis are relatively common, some are uncommon, but they all produce differing effects on the different types of joints. The point about arthritis is that many of them are generalized disorders in the body in which the most florid features are focused in the joints, rather than being just purely joint diseases alone.

The joint is lined by gristle which we call cartilage, and there's a fluid which lubricates the joint called synovial fluid, and a capsule which holds the whole thing together, and the lining of the capsule is called the synovium, and in arthritis the synovium becomes extremely inflamed and the surfaces of the joints become eroded, and you get a severe irregularity in the surface so that the joint doesn't work properly, it becomes very painful, and seizes up.

In my particular unit we've got a strong interest in back problems. Back troubles affect about two-thirds of the population at some time or other, so they are remarkably common. I'm involved in the study of the spine and the mechanisms of why people get back pain.

Almost everybody over the age of fifty has got evidence of wear and tear problems, but not everybody suffers from back pain. In other words there's more to it than just the mechanical wear and tear. And there's good evidence now that associated with these mechanical problems is secondary inflammation and fibrosis which follows the damage, and this is probably responsible for the pain in a large proportion of the patients. We have found that in many of these patients with severe chronic back pain there is a deficiency of enzyme in the blood. Enzymes are like the biological enzymes in washing powder that remove biological dirt from clothes: enzymes in blood remove biological dirt from the tissues, in this case fibrin, and because of this deficiency, the fibrin accumulates, and this is associated with inflammation and fibrosis of the tissues.

There are problems which particularly tend to occur at the lowest level in the spine. The spine consists of a pile of vertebrae, one on top of each other, lying on top of the tail bone. And the tail bone is tilted so there's a wedge between the back of the tail bone, the sacrum, and the lowest, or the fifth lumbar vertebra, and the disc which lies between the two is the most subject to wear. So that does appear to be a design fault, perhaps associated with the upright posture. There's not much you can do about it, but it's a problem.

Considering that it's got to last you for seventy years, that it's got to bend and twist and to convey nerves and to be able to repair itself – I think the spine is a fantastic structure. With all the wonders of modern engineering, you could not design a spine artificially with those constraints.

Knowledge has advanced enormously over the last few years. We've also advanced in studying the mechanics of the spine as well. Up to now a lot of that work was being done on dead spines in experimental situations, but the big advance in spine work has been the new forms of diagnostic imaging, new methods of seeing inside the spine. Until the last five or ten years, all we had were x-rays, and x-rays were very poor guides to what is happening inside the back, the problem being that x-rays only shadow the bony structures of the back, and because the spine is deep inside the back, you really only get a very poor view of what's going on inside. Now we've had big advances with two things: the first is computerized axial tomography or C A T scans, which are computerized x-rays of the back, which allow you to see detail inside the spine which was impossible to see before. A newer technique is called magnetic resonance imaging, or M R I. That doesn't involve x-rays at all but a very intense magnetic field in which you put the patients and you can actually get pictures of the soft tissue inside the back. This is an even bigger advance and we're only just beginning to exploit it at the moment.

I think one of the big problems is that a lot of people have a rather nihilistic attitude towards rheumatic disease; they think that there's not much that can be done for arthritis, and much of that has arisen through lack of proper treatment. You see, the most effective treatment for arthritis is to treat it early, before serious damage has occurred. Once a joint is severely damaged or eroded, you can do all the wonderful medical treatment in the world, but you can't restore that joint back towards normal. So the proper treatment is to treat these patients before they get permanent erosion of the joint surfaces.

And far too commonly, the patient's just been given some pills and told to get on with it, and then two years later they've developed severe deformities and crippling, and the damage is well under way. And once it's under way, it's a self-perpetuating process. I frequently find patients who go to their general practitioner complaining of rheumatic problems in their back or their knee and all that happens is that they get written out a prescription without ever being examined properly; you know, 'Just take some anti-inflammatory drugs', without specifically diagnosing the problem.

One of the essentials is proper diagnosis, and that requires certain techniques and examination. And I do think we need to improve the standard of rheumatic care in the general practice. In many cases it is good, but there are an awful number where it isn't, and so we are trying to improve general practitioner education, and most of us do quite a lot of lectures to GPs and demonstrations and that sort of thing.

A lot of paramedicine comes into rheumatology – patients take themselves off to non-medical practitioners of various sorts, osteopaths, chiropractors, herbalists, Christian Scientists, they might use copper bracelets and charms, I mean, there are 1,001 things like that around. And when you're dealing with chronic disease, one can quite understand that. But a lot of these conditions are subject to natural relapses and remissions, and of course you go and see someone when it's bad, and then quite often you get better around that time, so there's a tendency to think the chap must have done you good! A lot of what's done, like mud and wax and heat therapy and so on, is very nice and comforting and relaxing, but it doesn't actually make any difference to the underlying problem.

There are all sorts of strange ideas that some people have. I had one patient, a barrister, and he thought that his back pain was all due to rubber-soled shoes attracting static electricity in the body, and he fixed a wire down the back of his leg and trailed it behind him on the floor! Amazing!

I'm a firm believer that if you treat patients thoroughly and adequately early in the disease, you can control the disease and prevent most of the problems for the majority of patients.

DR JENNY LAW

GENERAL PRACTITIONER (LONDON)

═══════

THIS is a new health centre which was built by West Lambeth
Health Authority. My partner arrived on her own as a single-
handed GP, and three months ago, the two of us went into
partnership together, and we pay rent to the Health Authority for
the use of the premises.

I would say this particular estate is pretty typical of outer
central London, with a few fairly up-market bits where there are
nice Victorian or Georgian terraces, and the odd bit of greenery,
but not much, and the usual high street shopping, Kentucky
Fried Chicken, that kind of thing.

Our patients are mainly from the lowest social classes, a very
tiny minority of middle-class people, stolid Lambethians who
have grown up and lived in this part of London all of their life;
we have a lot of Indians, Asians, Bengalis, a few Vietnamese,
quite a few Irish people, and a lot of West Africans, mainly
Nigerians. And quite a few down-and-outs, because there's a big
men's hostel in our area, with a lot of middle-aged men with
psychiatric and alcohol problems. So we see quite a lot of deprivation and poverty.

Well, the biggest problem generally with the down-and-outs is
alcoholism. And the immediate problem for us is that they often
come to the surgery drunk, where they can be abusive to our staff
and frighten the other patients – and that's one thing that does
upset us, because it upsets everybody else here, and also because
it means we can't have a sensible conversation and make any
plans with them, or discuss what their needs or problems actually

are. So we tell them to come back sober, we won't see them when they're drunk. A lot of them have such a chronic alcohol problem that realistically the hope of achieving much and helping them to stop drinking or even modify their drinking is zero.

If they're on pills that we would rather not prescribe to them, we try and wean them off those. I'm sorry to say, I think indiscriminate prescribing by previous doctors has got them addicted to tranquillizers of various sorts, and so there's a high dependence on tranquillizers in that group, and they find it difficult to understand a new young doctor coming along and saying, 'No, I don't want to prescribe these for you.'

And then we actually give them a decent physical check. They have a lot of foot problems, for example, which are to do with hygiene: yuckie athlete's foot and lacerated skin, and toenails that have got imbedded because they've never had them properly cut. And a host of skin problems: you know, lice, infestations, that sort of thing. I don't mind what anybody looks like, that doesn't bother me, but I find coping with an extremely nasty smell fairly difficult. It's not the person themselves who repulses me, it's just because it's very unaesthetic, and I happen to think, you know, people who smell revolting, smell revolting!

A lot of GPs screen patients before they'll accept them on their list, and if they're smelly and dirty and drunk, they're not very keen on signing them on. So the choice is not actually all that great for them, and we are one of the few practices around here who don't mind registering these people or looking after them.

With the Asian population, fever is a very common presenting complaint. They have a very high expectation of being given some kind of treatment, a prescription or an injection. I frequently try not to prescribe, and that's a potential source of conflict for the patient and me, because they may feel dissatisfied I haven't given them something to take when they leave. I have the feeling that they expect a rather paternalistic or didactic doctor to say, 'This is what you're going to do, take the medicine, and off you go.' But part of my training has been to ask the patient what *they* think is wrong with them, and they clearly find that a fairly extraordinary question: 'Well, that's why I've come to you. You tell me.' Language is another problem. A lot of the Asian women don't speak English, and if you're trying to discuss any kind of gynaecological or contraceptive problem, that can be quite difficult. Their husbands often speak better English, but they won't come in with them. I suppose the language thing in some ways is the primary problem because communication is everything, and if we can't communicate, it's like veterinary medicine at the end of the day, and unsatisfactory for everyone. The other thing is a lot of them do have quite large families and live in pretty squalid conditions; they haven't got adequate heating, three or four children all cramped in a tiny little bedroom and appalling diets as well.

Home visits are fascinating because it gives you a chance to go into somebody's home where ordinarily you'd have no access, and it really is a vision to go and see how some people live. There are the most impeccable and tidy homes that one would never have imagined from seeing them come into the surgery. But one also picks up a lot of clues about somebody's health problems by seeing what's going on at home. When you go and see what the home situation is, you can suddenly understand why somebody might be stressed or anxious, when you could never work it out when you're sitting face to face in the surgery.

Every so often I see the most disgusting, disgusting poverty. You know, literally when there's an old lady who lives with no electricity, no water, maggots in her mattress, you can see the sky through her ceiling, she's only fifty-five but she looks about seventy, filth around the flat, but she wants to stay where she is, she doesn't want to be moved out.

I suppose there's a fairly high consulting rate for what I would call minor illness, and a lot of stress-related symptoms; the general inner-city problems of housewives with depression and anxiety, oversized families, not enough money to feed the kids, nowhere to put them into nursery so they can't go out to work, that kind of thing. I mean, you notice that people come in quite often, and you think, 'Why do they keep on coming in? OK, the kid's got a cough, but the kid's all right', and there's obviously something underlying, some kind of anxiety.

There's definitely quite a lot of problem with IV drug abuse. My partner and I have slightly different views on this. We have to be quite careful, because if any practice is known to be sympathetic to drug addicts, we would have a queue going from here to Westminster Bridge. A lot of people come in and ask us to supply them with certain things to try to keep their heroin or whatever use down. My partner always refuses to prescribe any kind of tablet and says that if they need help we will refer them to a drug dependence unit where they can be fully assessed. But part of the problem is that all the drug dependence units in London are pretty well oversubscribed. My personal feeling is that in the very exceptional case where I feel that I can make what I call a contract with a person about how and what I'm going to prescribe, I'm occasionally prepared to do it, but we're very wary and cynical about drug addicts, because basically they will tell you the most fantastic stories to try and get pills out of you.

Some people think of a doctor as being a fairly prestigious thing to be, but in the eyes of my patients I would say there's no great prestige attached to being a doctor, and I have the feeling that a lot of them just feel that we're here to give them a service. But on the whole, I'm treated very well and with respect. Sometimes people make comments about my age, that I'm a bit too young and not wise enough – perhaps when I get a few more grey hairs the situation will improve! But it's difficult to tell because face to face people are usually pretty polite, and what they might say to my receptionist outside will be quite different from what they'll say to me: they could be abusive to the receptionist about having to wait to see me and give her a hard time, and then they'll come in and be sweet as pie to me.

There's no question that work encroaches on my private life. But I accept it at the moment because I'm young and just beginning, and we're getting ourselves organized – and it won't always be like this, and later on I will have more time at home and to myself.

I'm not one of these people who lives and breathes medicine. When my day is over, I would like to switch off and not be medical and not be a doctor, but just be Jennifer Law doing what interests me after work.

But in fact at the moment that's impossible. Jane and I have a very large list for an inner-city practice – we have nearly 6,000 patients, and we have made the decision to do all our own on-call, which means that we have to take it in turns to be on duty for emergency calls, which we do alternate nights and alternate weekends. Jane is away at the moment, she's on holiday in France, so I am on call every day, every night, twenty-four hours a day for the next two weeks. So I can't forget about it, I have to carry my bleeper with me, and I just can't switch off.

I find it quite a strain – not a physical strain, because, thank goodness, we're not called out that often – but a mental strain, feeling that anything you do, you might be interrupted. But, that's just me, I don't think every doctor would feel like that, and I don't think my partner does.

Sometimes I feel absolutely whacked and so exhausted that I don't want to ring anybody up, and then other times I feel if I'm working hard I should play hard as well. More recently I've been exhausted!

My boyfriend is a doctor as it happens, the first doctor I've ever gone out with. We're about to buy a house together. I find it very helpful, him being a doctor, because he completely understands my anxieties, and if I've made a decision which I'm worrying about, I sometimes say to him, 'What would you have done?' And if he says, 'It's all right, Jenny, I would have done the same thing', that makes me feel a lot better!

When I was a hospital doctor, after I left the ward at 6 o'clock, that was it, and I really did not want to think about work until 9 o'clock the next morning. But as a GP you feel that you have the ultimate responsibility for your patients. I mean, even when somebody's in hospital, they've still got a G P who's going to carry on being responsible for them. You know, when somebody goes in and has their breast removed and then gets sent home, we're the ones who have to pick up the pieces and counsel them, or cope with them when they get depressed or whatever. And I think that with G Ps, if they're conscientious G Ps, it does get woven into your life, and it's very difficult to switch off. And that's the only bit about being a G P that I have difficulty about, the feeling that I do want to switch off and not be at work. Somebody will see me on my way home, and shout out, 'The kid's got a rash. Shall I bring her in to see you?' I can't say, 'I have left work. I'm not wearing my doctor's coat. Don't ask me this question.' People expect you to be there and available. But I enjoy it, so it's all right . . . for the moment.

I think the thing that I'm most worried about is what you'd call burn out. I mean, I'm just doing too much now, I'm putting too much into it. You see, my partner and I share all the admin of the practice as well – we're effectively running a business and being G Ps at the same time, worrying about our staff, and doing boring things like P A Y E that nobody taught me to do at medical school. We now have to make the decision whether we want to expand the practice and take on another partner, or close the list and just stick where we are.

I think that in the past being a G P was often seen as the second option: people who'd failed to get further in hospital specialties went into general practice. But there's a very definite shift with people positively going into general practice as their first option now, and I think G Ps need to wave the flag a bit more to say that they are good doctors, and they've chosen to do it, they're not second-rate.

The best part of the job is when somebody thanks you for something that you've done. Either writes you a lovely letter saying how wonderful you are, or brings you in two apples for your lunch to say thank you, which just makes you think, 'Gosh, it's all worth it'; a pat on the back – it's what you need to keep going. This morning I had a phone call in the middle of surgery which was one of my West Indian patients who said she was ringing up to sing me a song over the telephone and thank me for the cream I'd given her for her rash, and she was going to pray for me to be wise and so on. I thought she was going to say, 'You're useless! The stuff you've given me is no good!' So that was nice.

DR SUSANNA LAWRENCE

GENERAL PRACTITIONER (LEEDS)

I THINK, looking back on it, I was fed a lot of romantic stuff about doing good and being a carer, and at school how I was good enough to be a doctor, therefore I ought to be a doctor. And I was also encouraged very much by my family to take up medicine. I was getting so much affirmation around from every-body about how wonderful it was to be a doctor that it seemed a great thing to choose. So I went into it without even questioning it.

Medical school was a series of shocks really. My first impressions were that I'd landed myself with a lot of rugby-playing, beer-drinking people that I didn't identify with at all. I'd been interested in feminism a few years before then on a sort of superficial level; you know, it made sense to me but I hadn't really looked into it, but I couldn't believe the woman-hating that went on. That was the biggest shock about medical school. Everything was geared towards the boys, and there was a lot of very difficult stuff for me to deal with. You'd have a lecture on the ankle, and there would be a slide put up on the screen of a woman with no clothes on, and this was supposed to be terribly funny. I really thought, maybe I'm making a mistake here. 'What does the woman with the big breasts think?' This was a consultant giving a talk around a patient's bed to medical students. A lot of stuff like that. 'If you care, you ought to have been a nurse, not a doctor.' That was later on. It was shocking really, very shocking.

You had to prove you were one of the boys, otherwise you were not accepted. Things like not complaining about working three days, and staying up for two nights on the trot in between while, and taking that and being able to do it. If you said, 'I'm not going to do this', then you're not good enough; 'Well, girls shouldn't do it anyway' sort of stuff. Certainly showing any emotion: you're supposed to go without being affected by patients' horrendous experiences or not show that you're affected by them.

I was amazed when I went to medical school to find out how little doctors actually knew and how much guesswork there was, and what really shocking things they were doing with people's bodies and people's lives on really often quite shaky evidence. And I think in order to trust somebody to do that, the general public has to think, 'Well, these people are very, very special and do have enormous knowledge' – and they don't, it's a lie, it's a myth. But that myth is what helps people when they do get better, it's the so-called placebo effect, which is very, very effective.

At the moment, I do GP locums, temporary work. I'm not particularly interested in working in hospitals now, I find it alienating, and I don't think that's where the most important health care goes on. I appreciate that it's very specialized and very clever and very important, but for most people, primary health care is where it's happening.

Locum work is something I wanted to do. I've been doing contract jobs six months a year for the last five years, doing things I wanted to do, and working when I choose really. And it's a good idea for lots of reasons. For one, it gets me enough outside of the system to be able to appraise it critically and see what I actually want to be doing in the next ten years or whatever, and it also means that I can work in lots of different places, get a lot of ideas about different ways of doing things, and also gather lots of different experiences.

Last week I was working in a hospice where I've worked on and off for five years, standing in because the director was away on holiday. This week I'm doing two family planning clinics. Next week I start working in a very interesting practice in

London, a collective feminist general practice, and so quite un-usual from that point of view. After that I'm coming back up to Leeds, and I'm joining a cervical screening programme, basically offering a well woman's service to women in the workplace rather than waiting for them to come to the doctor.

I suppose feminism is important to me; I mean, it's quite central to my life. Women's health is something that I feel is very badly done by the medical profession generally, and I think that a feminist perspective has a lot to offer in improving women's health care. I see the medical profession at the moment as very paternalistic: 'We'll take the responsibility, *you* don't need to know what's going on.' But there's a whole trend towards sharing more information, allowing people to take responsibility for their own health, and that makes sense for men and women.

It's very clear that things aren't good enough at the moment – for men as well as women. I mean, I have a feminist perspective, but men suffer from paternalism, you know, men are stuck in a stereotype sex role just as much as women are; it's like men never go to the doctor, men aren't allowed to be sick, men aren't allowed to feel insecure and upset and unsure, they're not allowed to cry, and all of those things affect their health.

And the stereotype for women is that they are neurotic, they have lots of little problems they're always bothering the doctor with, and that they are very bad at giving histories and telling the truth.

Well, certainly you can say that the worst health is in the worst social conditions – that's blatantly clear. People who live in poor social conditions have appalling health.

I worked in Meanwood Valley, which has some appallingly bad estates, a lot of houses that are falling down but still lived in, some very, very poor social conditions: broken windows, babies coming home from hospital without any clothes, wrapped in bits of paper, and stuff I had no idea still went on.

I mean, when I was working in a middle-class Leeds area, a lot of people used to come just to discuss a problem, they didn't particularly want a prescription, it was a very much more nego-tiable consultation; you know, this is the problem, can we discuss it? The health centre was a comfortable, carpeted place, the whole atmosphere was very middle class really.

Meanwood was very different. A lot of, 'Well, you're the doctor,' you know, 'here's the problem, *you* deal with it.' People really not being in a position to take any responsibility for their health at all. There was a lot of us following up people who we knew needed some sort of health care team, be it district nurses or what have you, rather than waiting for them to come to the door, because basically we knew that they just wouldn't come to us if it was left to them.

Things like a woman who came in with a poorly shoulder who had been bleeding on and off vaginally for four or five years. And just as she was leaving, she said, 'Oh, by the way, is this the change?' And she turns out to have an advanced cancer of the cervix. She knew vaguely about smears but didn't really know what it involved, it sounded frightening, and she didn't know that it was connected to the particular symptoms she was having. Another woman whose son I saw for a long time, he used to talk about how she was a bit batty, never got out of bed and kept throwing herself on the floor, and there wasn't much point in visiting. And when I actually went there and examined her, it turned out she was very, very anaemic and grossly neglected, and if she had been seen by any health worker in the previous three years, anybody just looking at her would have noticed that she was anaemic, and would have done something about it. But she just hadn't had any contact with anybody at all. And, I mean, it's those sort of illnesses, where things are just left, where early intervention would have helped a great deal. It's ignorance, but it's also a lot of fear, a lot of 'I don't want to bother the doctor', a lot of acceptance of their lot. That's the common denominator amongst people at the bottom of the triangle: they just expect a great deal of ill-health. The coughs! 'Oh well, I smoke.' But these are rip-roaring chest infections, and examining them, it's clearly an ongoing bronchitis or even a pneumonia. Things like that, and to them it's like it's acceptable in some way: that ill-health is to be put up with.

The worst situations are the ones where I feel completely helpless: somebody with severe disabling arthritis who is not going to get better, who is going to have to deal with a great deal of pain for the rest of their lives, and who is not adjusting at all. It's my own uselessness, that's what frustrates me more than anything. And there was one woman that I used to visit regularly who I used to feel so completely helpless with, she had had a stroke and she was disabled and she was bitter and angry: she'd been like that for ten years already when I went to see her. Her husband was going up the wall, he was ill himself, he had diabetes, and that situation was just fraught. She wouldn't go into a home, she had to depend on a rotation of the neighbours to look after her as she had to have somebody there all the time, and there was just nothing that I could offer there at all. Those situations where I know that somebody's health would be so much better if only their social circumstances were better are very frustrating, trying to get somebody moved and rehoused who really would be quite all right in a ground-floor centrally heated flat but who is just having one illness after another because they're still living with no heating high up in a tower block.

It's so clear that living in damp houses gives you chest infections, you can't argue with that, and two-thirds of the houses that I used to visit in Meanwood were damp, really very damp. Awful.

I think that traditionally in deprived areas, the doctor isn't considered somebody you would talk to. It's so different from my own childhood experiences of the family doctor being a friend and somebody you trust, who pops in and you can talk to and so on. That just doesn't seem to operate in the same way in inner cities. And then, of course, there are added complications where in group practices you often don't get continuity, you can ask for a doctor, and there's any one of six doctors coming to see you, and if there's a deputizing service, it's a complete stranger anyway.

I'm very aware of how much I'm needed. What I'm getting out of doctoring is huge, but I'm very, very clear that I am basically doing it for myself, and in the end we probably all do things for ourselves. Even Mother Theresa is probably doing it because of the satisfaction she gets from it; it's very hard not to be needed in the way that you get used to being needed and having that sort of affirmation all of the time.

I try not to define myself as a doctor; I'm already having to take on everybody else's expectations of who I am, plus the power stuff, you know, the top of the pile stuff, which is very isolating, and also it's very insidious. You start to believe that sort of thing; it's very easy to believe that you are actually a little bit better than other people when you're being told so day after day. I hear it in my parents' voices as I'm introduced to somebody – they're proud, you know, *Doctor* Lawrence. I'm quite happy to be respected, but I want to be respected for me and not because of the label that society has decided is an important and special one. It's very easy to be successful as a doctor in terms of how people see you, but it's easy to fail on your own standards.

DR GILLIAN McCARTHY

NEUROPAEDIATRICIAN

I AM one of these people who wanted to be a doctor from a very early age, and I am not quite sure why, because it is not in the family, but it was something that I decided I wanted to do and stuck to. My mother had quite a lot of illness, she had to have a nephrectomy when I was about twelve or thirteen, so perhaps it was partly that I wanted to be able to know what was going on and be more in control. I don't know.

I see children as soon as possible after they are diagnosed as having something long-term neurological, actually helping them to develop as far as they are able, and that means working with all the other professionals like physios and O Ts and teachers and so on. And I try to give some sort of long-term involvement, because a lot of parents with deformed children see lots of different doctors and don't get any continuity.

I think that the families of severely handicapped children often need someone to actually talk to them and spend some time with them, and in busy clinics it is often difficult to do that. Families react in a way that reflects their relationship, so that a family who are together and reasonably all right people will actually be able to work through what is needed and come out the other end, whereas if the couple involved are already in trouble, if their marriage isn't working very well, then the addition of a child with a handicap may have very negative effects. It is very in-dividual; I don't think any two families react in exactly the same way.

I see a whole range of children, but most of them have got

some quite complicated handicap like spina bifida, cerebral palsy or muscular dystrophy.

Spina bifida is a disorder where you have an abnormality of the spine; it doesn't close properly during development. Along with this, you usually have hydrocephalus, which means that they have too much CSF, cerebral spinal fluid, so their head swells up, and they have to have a valve put in. So they are children who have lots and lots of problems, they need help with their walking, their bladder and bowel control, some of them have learning problems, and they have a fairly high mortality rate throughout their childhood. They were one of the largest groups, but the instance is going down because this is one of the conditions that you can diagnose *in utero*, and so you can try and prevent it that way.

Cerebral palsy is the biggest group that we see of children with severe problems: the incidence is about two per 1,000 live births. Cerebral palsy can be anything from total damage, someone who can't do anything for themselves, to someone who just has a slight limp when they walk. They are children who are damaged at or around birth by anoxia, a condition in which the tissues receive inadequate amounts of oxygen, in this case not enough oxygen reaching the brain. You have got a much higher risk of this in very premature babies or at a difficult birth.

Chailey, where I work a lot of the time, is a hospital school in Sussex for physically handicapped children that has been around for eighty years. It tends to take children with very severe handicaps, it was where the children with polio and bone and joint TB went, and we had a lot of children with Thalidomide damage and spina bifida.

When I first went to Chailey when I was going to be interviewed for a job there, there were a lot of children with limb deficiencies, and I remember seeing a child who had no limbs at all, just arms three inches on one side and nothing on the other, and no legs from the bottom down. He was a very beautiful-looking little boy about eight or nine, and I found that very shocking. I was used to the other disabilities and abnormalities, but that really upset me.

There have been some children there who have been awful to look at. We had a boy who was born without eyelids and a peculiar unfused mouth, instead of having a mouth he had a cleft almost from ear to ear, he was really quite frightening. He was actually a very nice little boy, and he was very much loved by the staff who looked after him because in spite of looking like that he managed inside to project a very nice personality. He had been rejected by his family as they couldn't stand what he looked like. He was eventually fostered and adopted.

Life isn't fair. I have certainly learnt that over the last twenty years. I guess what I am trying to do is to make the best of whatever a person has got, both for them and for their families, and be positive about it rather than give up. But I do have a number of children with progressive diseases, and to actually watch someone with muscular dystrophy wasting away, and to go through that with a family you have known for over ten or fifteen years, that is very depressing, and I find it almost as sad as they do.

I'm probably too involved. People say you shouldn't get involved with your patients, but one of the things I think that makes what I am doing important is that I do actually get to know the families over a period of time, and therefore you are giving a bit of yourself to each family each time. If you don't do that I don't feel that you're doing the job very well, but it does mean that you get burned out. My husband and I go away every three months. He actually says, 'I have to take you away so that you cannot be got at and people can't reach you, just to get a break.'

I have to admit that we actually foster a child who was at Chailey, so my husband and I have got involved in a personal way. She is seventeen now. She has cerebral palsy and is very bright and verbally able, but she can't walk and doesn't move very much. I didn't intend to foster anybody, but it just evolved really, her need for a family and the fact that we didn't actually have any children. Her name is Sarah and she is very attractive, with dark hair and light-blue eyes. She has got a very nice personality, a very loving girl, she's all right.

There are times when things seem to come in on you. Recently there was a boy who had a very horrible condition called Lesch–Nyhan syndrome, which is a metabolic condition where patients have a terrible movement disorder and mutilate themselves. This boy had a very nice personality, and you could see inside there was somebody who was desperately trying to get out. But he became very ill and eventually he died just before Christmas. I found that very hard-going, just watching the way he suffered in the end. It was very difficult.

There are times when I don't understand why people have to suffer quite so much. I just trust that it is going to be all right somewhere.

DR COLIN McDOUGALL

LEPROLOGIST

MY wife's got very amused by this now, she's seen it happen so
many times, particularly at a cocktail party or over a dinner table:
the first thing that happens is that anybody talking to me about
leprosy, they usually ask five or six questions – all of which are
completely on the wrong tack, and reveal that they've got fundamentally wrong ideas about the disease. For instance, people
think that there's no more leprosy in the world. You know, 'I
thought the whole thing was finished long ago . . .' That's
wrong, of course. 'Obviously you have a vaccine, why can't you
vaccinate them all . . .?' Well, we haven't got a vaccine, so we
can't vaccinate them. 'I thought there were drugs to completely cure the few remaining cases . . .' and so on. And then
they think that it's very, very highly contagious and dangerous
and think that I must be terribly brave to be working with it,
which is not at all true. TB would be far more dangerous and
AIDS even worse, and I could mention half a dozen others –
rabies, snake bite venom and so on. These people really have got
to watch it.

It's a big problem. The World Health Organization estimates
11 to 12 million cases worldwide; main areas affected are the
Far East, India, the continent of Africa, and South and Central
America.

Leprosy is a very ancient disease, it's been around for a very,
very long time, you know, hundreds and hundreds of years
before Christ. And the treatment has always been a matter of
difficulty, because this leprosy bacillus has been totally impossible

to grow *in vitro*, that means to say in a laboratory culture, so this has gravely hampered the development towards vaccines and drugs.

The bacillus has this extraordinary propensity to enter not only the skin and various other organs but actually to enter the nerves, which is very unusual, it's almost unique. Now, once the bacilli enter the nerves of the immune system, they provoke a very nasty little battlefield, and that results in loss of sensation and loss of muscle power. The disease can affect the eye, the testicles, the bridge of the nose may be damaged, the nose may collapse, the skin of course is very, very widely affected, and so on. And because the ulnar nerve of the hand is damaged, you get secondary contractions, and the patient ends up with very nasty-looking claw and anaesthetic fingers. The image of limbs falling off leprosy patients is true, but that's actually something of a secondary effect, it's due to this process I've been describing whereby the organisms get into the nerve and then interrupt the fibres that give you sensation or muscular power, so you're left with an insensitive and paralysed limb.

And under Third World conditions, it isn't surprising that limbs get further damaged, infected or ulcerated, with loss of soft tissue, bone and so on. And that's what leads to the deformities.

Physically, leprosy sufferers can look quite revolting, and this aspect of the disease shouldn't be underrated, because if you have a heavily maimed patient with bilateral ulcerating feet and filthy stinking ulcers, and one of his eyes is half hanging out because his face is paralysed, and he's got awful nodules all over his face and body, this is a dreadful sight. And people do get very frightened, there's no doubt of it. Also, because the ulcers on his feet are not attended to properly, and the bandages are filthy and have flies all over them, there can be a terrible smell.

Through the centuries the most ghastly things have been done to leprosy patients; they've been victimized in a very terrible way. Quite a lot of them are turned into outcasts, rejected by society, and it's extremely difficult for them to get back. In some countries they've been buried alive, in other countries they've been chased out of the village into a hovel or hut which has then been burned down with the occupant at night, and so on and so on. The history of man's inhumanity to leprosy patients is very oppressive. You don't get that with TB or VD or diphtheria, and one isn't seeing it with AIDS actually. Perhaps we've become more civilized in that sense. Less of course in other ways – but in that sense we may have actually improved.

Perhaps I should have been more affected by so much suffering than I actually have. But I think, if I may suggest it, any doctor who doesn't get over that sort of thing fairly early on in his career, or nurse for that matter, is always going to be rather seriously handicapped when it comes to a cool-headed and useful contribution to the situation in later life. And whether I was never very sensitive about all these things, I don't know, but I must confess it's never been a worry to me.

Of course leprosy is very definitely contagious, but nobody quite knows how it passes from one infected human being to another. One very strong possibility is that it is a droplet- or aerosol-spread infection, very much like tuberculosis or measles or many other straightforward infectious diseases, and it is blown out from the upper respiratory tract of the patient with leprosy and inhaled, or otherwise taken into the nose or the lungs of the next susceptible person.

I suppose I could get infected, it is a possibility, but that's an occupational risk. My father was a tuberculosis physician and I was born in a tuberculosis sanitarium, as they were called in those days, and grew up in one, and I always knew that working with TB was a very worrying occupational risk, especially open, infectious cases – handling the sputum from TB patients you've got to be very careful what you're doing. Fortunately, touch wood, I don't think the level of occupational risk in leprosy is anything like in that order at all, and it's rather uncommon for a leprosy worker or doctor to develop the disease.

My father made an immense mark on me. I admired him very greatly. And when I came to qualify, and looked back at his obituaries and this kind of thing, I did realize that we had been in the presence of an outstandingly good chap who'd made major contributions in the world of tuberculosis in his day. And when I started my work on leprosy, I always realized that there are close similarities between the two diseases, they are brother and sister diseases. In fact, tuberculosis has at least 20 million sufferers on the books, but it's got a very fast turnover because of the death rate; people are constantly dying off with TB. I think I'm right in saying that there are 10 million new cases of tuberculosis every year. It's a very big problem.

For the past twenty years I've been working in Oxford in leprosy research, but I've worked in the Far East, which was tremendously interesting, one of the most interesting things I think I've ever done really. I came back to this country again and did some more post-graduate study to become a specialist in internal medicine, did a year at Bart's on the medical unit, but decided I wasn't cut out to become a kind of conventional National Health Service medical consultant, so I went abroad again. I'm not sure if you're aware of this, but there is a very high percentage of people who come to see a general practitioner in this country who in fact have got absolutely nothing physically wrong with them at all. They have symptoms which are described as psychosomatic. It's perhaps a little unfair to say that they're imaginary, but they have no definite basis in physical illness. And I found the enormous amount of this very depressing, and I realized as the years went by that I was psychologically very poorly equipped to make this my life's work. Others of course are marvellous at it, but I have never been.

I went to the Middle East as a medical specialist to work in the Queen Elizabeth Hospital, and saw a good deal more leprosy coming down from the Yemen, and then applied for a job as a leprosy specialist in Zambia, and I looked after leprosy for the whole country for three years. It was some of the most vivid medicine I've ever seen in my life.

I think, in essence, what intrigued me about these countries was that for the very first time in my life I suddenly realized that almost everybody you saw had serious organic illness. There was nobody with neuroses or hysteria or depression that nobody could do anything about; they were all sick people with a rather serious degree of leprology. And you could get to grips with this, and in many cases at least improve them, and I found this immensely satisfying, and it obviously fitted some sort of longing for a kind of pragmatic activity in my psychology, which I've noticed more and more markedly as the years have gone by.

I am rather surprised at how ignorant people are about their own personal physiology, what makes their heart beat and how many times they breathe a minute and all that kind of thing. I'm not surprised at their ignorance about leprosy, because after all, why should they know anything about leprosy?

If people knew more, doctors' status would diminish. Because in America, I don't know how they get the knowledge, maybe it's from Reader's Digest or something, they do know a hell of a lot more, so the doctors have a difficult time in talking about anything to the patient, they are constantly challenged in a way that would never happen in this country – patients just don't argue with us in the clinics here.

I think there is a very evident psychological change that comes over doctors rather early in their careers which leads to them being in a way very dependent on patients. I sometimes think that some of my colleagues have to have the doctor–patient relationship in order to feed their own ego. Of course, it's a little bit understandable in a way because very early on, when you begin to look like a doctor because you've just put your white coat on and there's a stethoscope hanging out of your coat pocket, patients do talk to you and depend on you in a most extraordinary way, a very touching way really, and they will ask you about things and respect your advice, and this obviously has an effect on us. Why we become so sort of pig-headed and autocratic later on, I don't know. That's most unfortunate.

I've been working in leprosy continuously for twenty-two years now, so it's been *the* major element in my medical life without any doubt at all. I suppose I've been fascinated by it. I

mean, leprosy is a terribly interesting disease, it is full of un-
knowns and mysteries and things that need to be resolved, and it
has challenges at so many different levels – sociological, environmental, microbiological, immunological, drug development – it's
got terrific potential for study really, and there's a lot to be done.

I would say without exaggeration that progress in recent years
has been absolutely astounding. And one of the main reasons is
that eight or nine years ago, WHO together with the United
Nations Development Programme and the World Bank all got
together and they created a thing called the Special Programme
for Research and Training in Tropical Diseases, and they chose
six diseases for very special attention, and to our enormous
benefit, leprosy has been one of them. And this has resulted in
astonishing progress towards the development of a possible vaccine for leprosy, and also to the very much better use of the
available drugs.

SISTER SUSAN McGUINNESS
NURSE

I TRAINED as a nurse before I became a nun. Nursing is a great way of expressing my particular way of life, and my vows enable me to spend more time with people than if I was married and had a family or a permanent relationship with someone.

I am employed as a staff nurse bereavement counsellor in an Accident and Emergency department. I do all the other normal nursing things in an A & E department, like stitches and putting plasters on and helping to resuscitate people, but perhaps the unique aspect of my post is that we offer bereavement counselling to the relatives of people who die in our department, which doesn't happen in any other A & E department in the country.

It is a caring kind of relationship, and my caring would be influenced by my faith: I belong to an order called The Faithful Companions of Jesus, and what I am offering the bereaved relatives whom I meet is companionship, which hopefully reflects the companionship that Mary experienced when she was at the foot of the Cross looking at somebody she loved, Jesus, dying. I am with people who are seeing someone they know and love, who gives meaningful purpose to their life, dying, and trying to make sense of that. That would be how I see it.

Some Sisters choose to wear a veil, but I don't, because it became unhelpful, basically, because when I was talking to relatives, a lot of their anger seemed to be directed at me, perhaps not at me personally, but me as John Paul II's personal representative in Salford's A & E department, and it was unhelpful for the relatives; they needed to get to their own grief in a sense.

It is very difficult to generalize the behaviour of bereaved people. People are very disorientated, extremely confused, and often disbelieve that the information you are giving them, particularly the news of a death. They're convinced that you have got the wrong person, it isn't actually *their* husband, wife, daughter or son. They are reluctant to accept the enormity of the situation. And extremely reluctant to accept that there are some things that we cannot do anything about. If somebody comes in with a transected aorta, the main blood vessel coming out of your heart, if it is cut, transected, it is incompatible with life. You are brain dead. But because of the myths surrounding modern medicine about curing illnesses and saving lives, people have enormous expectations, particularly in the casualty department and high dependent areas like ICU (Intensive-Care Unit) and coronary care. For instance, people read in the paper about heart or lung transplants, and wonder why we can't do something about their baby who has died, or their seventeen-year-old son who has got a smashed up brain because he has come off his motor bike.

Some reactions can be physically quite violent: banging their head against the wall or smashing the table. They can be verbally very violent about the person who has died, very violent towards the staff because they haven't saved the person's life, or very violent towards another member of the family who may be there. They can scream or faint, or they can just say nothing and sit there in absolute silence. Some people cry a lot, some won't cry. It seems to depend.

Then people react in different ways to the news of the death depending upon how well or how poorly they have been prepared. What used to happen was the relatives would arrive with the patient and be shown into a room and given a cup of tea. Twenty-five minutes later a nurse and doctor would come in. The doctor would stand up and the nurse would sit while the doctor told the relatives that the person has died, go out and leave the nurse to pick up the pieces of the relatives – really unhelpful for the relatives, real cop-out for the doctors. Basically there was no

training to prepare medical people for that moment of breaking
bad news. Bad news was really badly told, and the help and
support that relatives received was determined by things like
which side of the bed the doctors or nurses got out of that day,
how much time they had, how inadequate or vulnerable they felt
to speak to someone who was perhaps hysterical or not saying
anything, just silent. It is very easy for nurses and doctors to hide
behind a uniform and not to get personally involved.

I mean it's not really very funny, but an illustration of how
appallingly bad news is told is the use of clichés and jargon to
avoid saying things like 'dying' and 'dead'. One doctor, he used
to say, 'I'm afraid we've lost him', and time and time again
people would say, 'Where have you lost him? Has he gone to x-
ray?' We actively discourage the use of clichés and jargon here
because it's a cop-out from the nurse and doctor's point of view,
and it's stupid to use that kind of language when somebody's
already disorientated.

On a physical level, death in an A & E department or a
resuscitation area is often very traumatic. People end up in a resus
area because something tragic and unexpected has happened. Say
they've been involved in a road traffic accident, then because of
the circumstances of the death, the person may be very smashed
up and may not look very nice; they may be burnt, or mutilated,
or whatever, and you may need to do some quite invasive
procedures, i.e. a central venous line into the chest, or intubating
them, putting a tube down into the lungs, where you may
actually sever a capillary – and there will be plenty of blood
around. So sometimes people don't look too nice or beautiful.
You try to maintain their dignity by keeping their anatomy
covered up, but keeping them covered up isn't the priority; the
priority is to get their heart beating again and to get them breathing.

When I suggested to our medical staff that we bring relatives
into the resuscitation area, there were enormous objections. They
said things like, 'The relatives will go berserk when they see all
these tubes and machines.' But to date not one relative has gone

berserk, because from the relatives' point of view, they only see this person they know and love, they don't see the monitors and all the rest of it. I tell them that there are machines around the person and we need them to try and help to save his or her life, and not to be frightened of them. Obviously if someone has got a smashed-up head, we will put a bandage around it, we will do something to make every person look as presentable as possible. Sometimes they don't look very nice. You say to people, 'Your husband, because he hasn't been breathing for a while, isn't his usual colour, and that may frighten you – do you still want to come in?' The problem is that people who don't view the body are more likely to have a more prolonged grief process than people who do. They imagine that the person is going to look much more horrific than is actually the case and I have never seen relatives faint at the sight of the person who was injured if they have been prepared.

If we get the hospital chaplain down to come in and say some prayers because the relatives want the deceased anointed – that's really a gobstopper, especially from the doctors' and nurses' points of view, because it kind of reminds us that we're not just a medical trauma unit, trying to use different resuscitation techniques – it brings another dimension into something that up until that point had been purely medical.

I've seen lots of deaths that have been really horrific, really, really sad, and I felt quite frustrated that here I am committed to a way of life that is very much for the service of the Church, and I don't really have any answers to these profound questions that people are asking me like, 'Why has God let this happen to me?' and 'Why do bad things happen to good people?' It's my faith that I turn to to sustain me to go on asking the question: 'What is it all about? Why are these things happening to people?' But it isn't God that causes these things to happen, it's a fact of human life that because we have a finite existence, because our bodies are basically a machine that runs out, just like a car wears out, then things will happen to us. They aren't *made* to happen to us, we're not predetermined to develop cancer or a brain tumour, they're just a consequence of human life. But people can't accept that. They want to blame someone who very rarely answers back. And so God's a really good sitting duck, you can really have a good go at him.

I've blamed God loads of times. 'I'm really sorry for these people – why does it have to be like this for them?' But my way of coming to terms with all that is I find it really consoling that even Jesus had problems contemplating his own death. In the garden of Gethsemene the night before he died, he called out, '. . . If there is any other way than suffering and death, for me to carry out Your work, show me it! I'm really frightened . . .' and lots and lots of times I've been in the Garden of Gethsemene when I'm frightened by circumstances.

But after the moment of death, there's the resurrection. And you know, in my life I've spent time with people who have been really down, and eventually, hope, light, meaning, does come out of something that was hopeless, full of darkness. For the bereaved person, they are looking for meaning in the events that they find themselves in – which doesn't come immediately, I mean, it takes two to five years for someone to come to terms with and accept the consequences of that close personal bereavement.

I think spending time with bereaved relatives should be part of the skills of any nurse and doctor working in A & E departments. Nursing nowadays creates specialties, which is good in a sense, but you need to maintain some breadth in skills as well. I feel really angry that I spent four years training to be a nurse and no one ever provided me with any skills about how to spend time with bereaved people.

DR JOHN MACLEOD

GENERAL PRACTITIONER

(OUTER HEBRIDES)

———

My father had a single-handed practice on the island of North Uist, where I now practise. In fact, both my parents were doctors there, and my mother is still alive and lives over the fence from us.

My father had been the doctor here through terribly difficult times, through the thirties, through the Second War, and in the immediate phase afterwards, when people didn't really know what was going to happen or what they were going to do with themselves. He didn't have facilities, he was conducting home confinements, there weren't any antibiotics, no phones, no cars, people had poor housing. But he gave a superb service through all that time, which must have taken a lot out of him physically and mentally, and he kept himself up to date with things by going off on courses and learning, and keeping up his wide contacts with people.

The island is about ten by twelve miles, and 90 per cent of the population are Gaelic-speaking. The east side is rocky, with heather and acid soil, the middle of the island has masses of fresh-water lochs, then on the west side is sand thrown up from the Atlantic, which is what we call 'machair'. There are not many high hills, and there is peat everywhere, and it is really very, very fertile.

The people are very kind and very hard-working; they've got a good sense of values, and family means so much more to them than it does to people in big cities. If you hear somebody in Uist talking about their cousin, you might find that was way beyond what you'd ever considered to be a cousin. The family links are very, very strong, and there's great pride in the families.

They're mainly self-employed. This is the feature of people who live in a crofting community; they may well have a full-time job, but they have got the land as well, and with this system, people have now got security of tenure through their family and descendants, but without actually owning the croft. But because they have got to give their holiday to the land, and the shearing of the sheep, and the doing of the hay, that creates a problem – no one has a chance to get away from it all.

My wife and several of the other women say that it is a man's life, and like a lot of the island women, she wants out. She says that she wants 'on the boat' . . . wants away. She feels confined by being on an island, not being able to get into the car and go to the shops.

Those of us that are in isolated practice, we are a different breed. Of all the doctors in Britain, we are really the only ones who are actually living and working amongst our patients. Anything we do is within those people who are our patients. With a general practitioner in a town on the mainland, there might be somebody next door, or two houses down who is a patient on his list, but he tends to be living away from his patients in a different area altogether. The hospital doctor has got all sorts of buffers, he's got his registrars, he's got the nurse. We are face to face with things the whole time.

The people in our area have absolutely colossal respect for their doctor, and you are on a pedestal that you really have got to knock yourself off. It is a terrible job to get people to address me on straight first-name terms. They always tend to use the prefix 'doctor', and one is referred to as Doctor John all the time. They are tremendously considerate and courteous. If my phone goes at four in the afternoon or six in the evening, not just at two in the morning, most people will start off by saying, 'Sorry to trouble you doctor, but so and so has got . . . can we bring him in or can you see them?' which is rather contrary to what you hear from towns, where the doctor gets a virtual demand to visit.

My partner and I have only got 1,760 patients, and the age spread is similar to that of Bournemouth. Unfortunately, we are not getting enough births, because people are tending to limit their families; they used to try and have four or five children, but now I am afraid it is stopping off at two or three. One other thing which I am worried about for the future is that we have got a shortage of women in their fertile years (if I am allowed to say that kind of thing these days), and this lack of appropriate girlfriends or wives does create problems. Women amongst men tend to alter their pattern of behaviour, but we have not got enough women to control the behaviour of that age group of men, so they're a bit aimless, nothing much to go for, no kids, no prospect of getting on – and the dram seems the easiest thing.

I have got my own ECG machine, I have got a blow tube in case someone has asthma, but one thing I miss is the ability to have someone's chest x-ray on the box in front of you within the half-hour. But we have got the little hospital at South Uist, where there are x-ray facilities, and a surgeon, so that knees and ankles, shoulders and hips can be dealt with there. And we have got a super air ambulance service, and I can call for that aeroplane and it will come with a nurse from Glasgow and take the patient straight to Glasgow Hospital within about four hours from me seeing the patient and making the decision to call them out.

I think that many of our people have a way of coping with life's problems themselves. There is certainly not the tendency for them to rush down the road into the doctor's surgery that there would be in a town. Quite a number are very religious and will use prayer or Bible. Religion is a form of medicine – it always has been. And if you have got a good parish minister, the doctor's work is lessened very much, and there is not enough credit given to this today. Our pastor, John Smith, is a super nice chap and a first-rate parish minister. Between ourselves he is a bit boring as a preacher, he goes on too long and pads it out to the twenty-eight minutes, but his first fifteen minutes are great.

Because the majority of patients are dying in their own homes, we see a lot of death. We are back and forward to their house if somebody is dying slowly; if someone dies suddenly, they are not taken in an ambulance to a mortuary, we are the ones who are called and go out and are there on the spot. In relation to our number of patients, we are seeing more deaths and are far more closely involved with death than a doctor in the town would be.

With our people there is a very clear acceptance of the time has come, and there would be a reluctance to have too much done unnecessarily to counter that. If it in any way seems that death is appropriate in the situation, there is no real upset at all amongst anybody. It is calm and even jocular. The neighbours will come into the house and sit and have a cup of tea, and even after the death has taken place, they may be weeping, which we encourage, but they will be talking about the super things that this bloke did or the amusing things about him or something of this sort. I think you may find things here a little different; there is less gloom and despondency about death at this end of the Hebrides.

I have come across death so often now. I have a feeling myself that there is 'a departure'. I see a change in people when they are dying. Many people get the feeling that this is quite absolute, that they are going, and I also feel that the nice features that you see in someone who has died haven't been fixed by the manner in which the nurse or the undertaker put their face in position or pad out the cheeks or lift the chin. There seems to be a quite definite serenity come over people at a certain time: now, whether it is before or during or after spiritual departure, I have no way of knowing, but there certainly seems to be.

You will have this one day if you haven't been present at a death before now, but the terminal stages from a stroke can be very distressing to the family, particularly to people who have not been near a death before. It can suddenly become quite noisy with very noisy breathing as the patient loses control of the larynx. Then the breathing pattern changes with long, long pauses of no breath, and then suddenly a few fast breaths, and then again, a long, long pause. You can be sitting in the next room waiting and listening and wondering if that is going to be the last breath, and you are just getting up from the chair to come through, and suddenly you hear it starting again.

I'm more and more hoping that at least one of my children will become doctors. It's very important to me personally, I feel very strongly about it, I'll do everything under the sun to persuade Alistair and Tarquin. The medical profession has for several years not encouraged enough of its own to come back in. People applying for medical school are being advised not to say that they have medical relatives. I suppose they think that the chap is just coming in because of his family. But I feel that there is a tradition of service amongst medical families, and that is all for the good.

What I want for North Uist is that they'll always have a good doctor. Other places, I couldn't give a dash what sort of doctor they have. But I think the people in North Uist really deserve good medicine, good care. It would be lovely to think that the tradition did continue.

DR GEOFFREY MAIR
GENERAL PRACTITIONER (SUFFOLK)

HALESWORTH is a small market town with about 4½ thousand people. It has a core of people who have lived here for generations and feel very Suffolk-orientated.

It's a rapidly growing town, because housing is fairly cheap, and retired people have been pouring in from London.

But people move up here with unreal expectations. They seem to have a nostalgic memory of happy family holidays by the sea in Suffolk, and they arrive here without having done any sort of basic research. There are no buses, for example, so they can't go shopping at Tesco's or Marks and Spencer's; and they often get very lonely and isolated, and then because they're in that age group, they become ill, and then they tend to blame the local community, and you sort of feel that perhaps they should have done some homework before they came.

I think the idea that people in the country somehow have a smaller number of social or psychological problems is a myth. People in the country very often are just as unhappy as people in a town. And in many ways they're less well catered for, they've got a smaller provision of self-help groups, social services aren't quite so thick on the ground. On the other hand, we haven't got any really bad housing problems, we haven't got any racial problems or any significant drug problems – although there are two or three heroin addicts in the practice.

The practice extends in a circle from Halesworth. It goes towards the sea at Walberswick, but not to Southwold, then inland as far as Laxfield and Northwoods, so it's about eight

miles in every direction. There are five of us in the practice and
9½ thousand patients, so that's about average for the county. Half
of them are in the town, half of them are in the country, and we
see the vast majority here at the Health Centre, where we each
see, I should think, about thirty people a day. There's the constant
business of trying to improve our preventative services: we do
quite a lot of screening, calling people in for various checks,
trying to make sure that we are developing much better systems
for disease indexes and that people are regularly surveyed if
they've got a thyroid disease, and that sort of thing. And because
of our isolation – we're thirty miles from the nearest district
hospital – we do a lot of other things; we do police surgeon's
work and school medicals, we do factory work, we look after a
large geriatric hospital three miles away – anything medical that's
going, we'll do.

When you've only got one practice in a town, people have to
feel they have a choice, and because we're all very different in our
practice, we hope people can have a good choice between us.
We're politically all very different in the practice, and we talk
about politics quite a lot. I'm not the most left-wing person by
any means, but I'm certainly left of centre. I'm not very good
with what you might call very upper-class patients. I'm not very
tolerant of people who seem to be trying to buck the system by
going privately and jumping queues.

I spend a lot of time doing my job, and inevitably it extends
home as well, not only through being on call but through living
in an area where everybody I see is a potential patient. Sometimes
I don't feel free to move about. I mean, there's a total lack of
anonymity in being a country doctor really, everybody knows
who you are, and while that means you can go shopping without
even taking any money – 'Oh, that's all right, you can pay me
later, doctor', sort of thing – on the other hand, you're never
actually free.

But all doctors start off with a lot of built-in good feelings
towards them, I mean, that's a built-in placebo right there. I
think a GP should be respected like any sort of competent

person, if they are competent, but not just because they're a G P. But there are still people around here who call you 'sir' whenever they see you, touch their cap, it's quite extraordinary.

Somehow being a G P is so kind of time-consuming and all-embracing that you never stop and think, what would I do if I wasn't doing medicine? I mean, I've got a patient who makes violins and I often think, 'Well, that's really the thing . . .' But I don't even know if I could make anything.

I think the public's level of awareness about their own health is increasing, but it's an untapped resource. People got the message about AIDS pretty quickly; they've got the message about diet to some extent, although you wouldn't think so going around the supermarket. But people don't seem to know the first thing about the idea of self-limiting illness, that a cold is a virus and you don't need an antibiotic for it. I mean, we should do a lot more educating people that a cold or flu will get better on its own. We have quite a lot of American patients, because we've got so many American bases around here, and you notice the difference in the way Americans perceive their illness – they're much more informed, sometimes irritatingly so, but they are much more knowledgeable.

Then there's the whole tranquillizer thing, and people asking for sleeping tablets. People find not sleeping tremendously distressing, and if you have the power to help them sleep, sometimes it seems very perverse not to. Ideally, if it's a new problem, you've got to try very hard to find out why they're not sleeping. I mean, they might be having acute worry, marital problems, depressive illness, stress, that sort of thing. But some of them get extremely angry if you don't give them the tablets – the pressure is phenomenal.

The trouble is that if you are running half an hour late and there are ten more people out there, and someone comes in coughing up a bit of spit or really feeling pretty rotten, it will take hours longer to convince them that you're not being negligent in refusing them an antibiotic than to just give it to them. So very often I just give medicine that I know isn't strictly necessary.

I've got a patient in her mid-seventies who still takes amphetamines – she was put on them maybe thirty years ago. Now that's a good example of a conflict. I would never dream of putting people on amphetamines now, but she takes one a day. I've talked to her endlessly about stopping these amphetamines – and the actual grief and pain it causes her when I talk about stopping them, or when I only give her twenty-five to last her for thirty days, and she has to choose five days not to take them – it's ruining her life. I make her come every month, poor thing, she doesn't get a repeat card, so she has to trot down here. She takes up a consulting time, and every month I go through the ritual: 'Don't you think you can stop these?' 'No, I couldn't possibly . . .' It's a problem.

We know an awful lot of technical things about doing heart transplants, and wonderful things about putting in artificial hips and things like that. But we don't know very much about why things happen to people when they happen.

Quite understandably, hospital doctors are having to become pure scientists – the machinery they're using and the ever more complicated investigative tools are incredibly complicated – whereas our tools of the trade aren't really very different than they've always been. And so there is a widening gulf between hospital doctors and general practitioners. I do feel that hospital doctors should do a period of training in general practice in the same way in which it would be impossible to be a GP without having done some hospital work.

I'm a passionate believer in the NHS. I mean, I think a doctor's a lucky man if he doesn't have to charge a person or think too much about whether a course of action is going to cost somebody something. But I'm becoming increasingly upset about the way people are treated in hospitals, in outpatient departments: the waiting, the rudeness, the lack of explanation that people seem to get.

I think medicine will change tremendously. There will be an increased realization that money has to be spent on health education and lifestyle changes: you know, putting a lot more effort into teaching people not to smoke and to take more exercise and that sort of thing. I think non-medical people will take on an increasingly important medical role: physiotherapists, counsellors, psychologists, people like that, and I think the doctor, particularly the hospital doctor, will decline. G Ps might decline as well. I mean, a lot of people *I* see could equally be seen by good nurses or psychologists or physiotherapists.

I'm pretty well totally atheist and I think I always have been; certainly nothing has happened to me in the last few years that has changed that. So many people die despite what you do, and I think we try and postpone death far too long. I increasingly have come to the view that when people genuinely say, 'If I get to be a cabbage, I would like to be helped to die', I really do feel we've got to tackle that. It's the sort of thing you wouldn't let happen to a dog. It really should apply to human beings; the load on caring relatives looking after terminally ill people is frightful. And on the whole I see death as being for a lot of people a tremendous release actually.

MISS AVERIL MANSFIELD
VASCULAR SURGEON

═══

I JUST always intended to be a doctor from as long as I can remember back. And not just a doctor, but a surgeon was my intent. I honestly don't know why. I think I said as much to my mother, who very sensibly replied, 'That's not something you should talk about, it sounds big-headed, it would be much better to say you want to be a nurse, and not sound as if you're aiming for higher things.' I'm from a working-class background: that's not a nice way to describe it, is it? But, you know, fairly humble origins. Nothing to do with the medical profession, certainly.

My first house surgeon's job after I graduated was working under a surgeon called Edgar Perry, who did one of the first vascular procedures in this country, and it fascinated me, and from then on I was directed towards vascular surgery.

I've often felt that it was because it didn't require great intellect to understand what was going on. I mean, I have frequently said to people I'm a glorified plumber, because in my job we either replace bits of piping that have got furred up or we bypass them, or something of that sort. It's very straightforward to understand what's gone wrong and to understand what's needed. It later becomes evident that it's not so easy to make the right decisions at the right time, but that comes with experience. And you get immediate results, which I like – I like to know for sure that we've got it right, and if you haven't, you go on until you do.

Just let me talk to you about your anatomy, in case you don't know what it consists of. The heart is in the centre of it all, blood is circulated to your body through the arteries and returned to your heart through your veins, and all of that is the vascular tree. Now, in this country, conventionally, we have cardiac surgeons who operate on the heart and the heart alone, and vascular surgeons who operate on the rest of it. That's me. So we operate on all of the blood vessels that are taking blood out into your brain, your arms, your kidneys, your gut, your legs, and then to a much lesser extent, and certainly to a much less complicated extent, on the veins that carry it back. And that's the nubbings.

The veins are the relatively minor side of the problem. Most of the serious operations are on the arteries. Some of them are very deeply inside you in your chest or abdomen, and some, like the radial pulse in the wrist, are practically under the skin. When you expose an artery, it's pulsating, because it's got blood flowing through it, so there are two steps that we have to follow then. One is to give the patient an anticoagulant so that when we stop the blood flowing, the static blood won't form a clot; then we stop the blood flow by clamping the artery. And when it's all static and the whole thing is still, it looks like a rounded tube, like a bit of piping, which we then either open up and clean out, or sew a bypass graft on to it.

I think by far the commonest operation I do is on the person whose arteries are blocked up in their legs and can't get enough blood to their muscles, so that they get pain when they try to walk, which we call intermittent claudication. If the arteries to the heart get blocked up, that would be angina, same thing, only it's the muscle of the heart not getting adequate blood supply, and the pain on exercise would be in the chest.

Then we might have a person who has what we call a transient stroke, and that indicates that the blood supply to the brain has become furred up, and circumstances being right we would then go and unbung it, clean it out, if you like, and restore normal circulation to the brain.

The acute interruption of the circulation to any part of the body is an important feature of our lives. For example, in road traffic accidents, motorcyclists seem particularly prone to rupturing arteries. It's awful for the person, but it's rather nice for the vascular surgeon, because then you have perfectly healthy normal arteries to deal with, which is the only time in your life you ever do, which have just been knocked into two halves by an injury.

But the thing that takes up most of our emergency life in vascular surgery is a thing called an aortic aneurysm. The aorta is the main artery that comes out of your heart and through your chest and abdomen to distribute the blood everywhere, and it is carrying a huge volume of high pressure blood. And that can develop a ballooning which, if we allow it to get too large, will burst – and if it bursts then your chances of survival are very small. The problem is that a lot of people don't get symptoms at all until it bursts, it's a real worry. Some get back pain and some get abdominal pain, but just once in a while you find somebody who has actually found this great pulsating lump in their abdomen and goes and seeks advice about it. They occupy a good deal of our time because they're commonplace in the older age group, and as we're getting older as a nation, so we have a lot more aneurysms.

The rest of the time we're dealing with arteries that are getting older and thicker. What happens is you build up these sort of fatty deposits inside the wall of the arteries, a sort of yellowish material, a bit like porridge in a way, called atheroma, which I think means gruel. We're all building them up, I fear – even you at your tender age! And in most people that doesn't matter very much, but if it builds up to such an extent that it narrows the lumen, the centre core of the artery, so that the blood flow is interrupted, then that becomes a stenosis, and cuts off the supply to wherever it was meant to be going to. There is some belief that altering your fat intake might make it a bit better, but basically once you've got it, you've got it.

As far as actual disease of the arteries is concerned, there is some evidence that perhaps modern living has produced more in the way of arterial disease, but there's much dispute as to which aspect of modern life is responsible. The Americans have gone overboard about exercise and all this sort of thing, but it's probably a combination of stress, and fats, and smoking. I think probably the best you can do is just try to be somewhere near your ideal weight, not smoke, and if you have high blood pressure, get it treated, and I don't know what to say about fats, I never do know what to say about fats.

But I've often said that if it were not for cigarettes, I would be on the dole. I mean, I do believe that vascular disease is primarily a smoking problem; it causes arteries to silt up and accelerates this process of atheroma in the wall of the arteries, and really it is a rare day when we come across somebody who's got severe obstruction to the blood flow who has not smoked significantly during their life.

You ask if anyone can just go in and have their arteries cleaned up. It sounds lovely, doesn't it? It might come one of these days, but not yet. I did some research on it years ago, but at the moment anything that could remove those fatty deposits from the arteries has got harmful consequences. We wouldn't embark on that sort of an operation unless it was needed, because any operation of that magnitude carries risks, and those risks have to be justified.

We all know about the heart pumping blood out, and nobody ever stops to question how it gets back. But, especially in somebody tall like myself, how is the blood down in my foot meant to climb all the way back to my heart without a pump? And in fact what happens is the muscles in your calf act as a sort of peripheral heart really; in the calf muscle are big veins, and when you contract your calf muscle it squeezes the vein and pushes the blood back to the heart. And it is aided in that direction by a series of valves which the veins contain (and the arteries do not), which are designed so that the blood can only flow in the direction of the heart. So it goes swoosh, stop, swoosh, stop, climbing up these valvular channels, and if one of those valves gives way or becomes incompetent, then the blood kind of goes backwards and forwards in the vein instead of going up to the heart, and that means the vein gets bigger and becomes a varicose vein. It's not of any great consequence, because the only veins that get that sort of trouble are the ones on the surface, and the big veins rarely fail. We're over-endowed with veins, we have millions of them, thousands anyway, and the ones on the surface, which are the ones that become visible as varicose veins, are really not vital to life, but that can be a big nuisance in terms of symptoms and appearance.

My husband's a general surgeon, and he's got an interest in vascular disease too. We talk quite a bit about work actually. I often say to 'my boys' at St Mary's – I'm awfully sorry, I always refer to my boys, meaning my registrars and house surgeons and students, it's my terrible habit – that I can get a little secret help at home if I'm just a little unsure of what should or should not be done in a situation. It is very valuable at times to sit over the breakfast table and say, 'I'm going to do this today, and I thought I might do *this*, what do you think?' And you get a good sensible discussion. Of course, at the end of the day I'm the person who makes the decision as to what happens   you couldn't be a surgeon unless you make decisions fairly easily. But even so there are times when in your heart of hearts it's difficult to be quite certain which is the best way to proceed, and it's very nice to have the chance to try it out, one to one, as it were.

The abdomen is the commonest place we get into, and we cut through first the skin and then the muscle, and then into the peritoneal cavity, which is a sort of sack that contains the guts: there's no difficulty at all, you're in there in seconds.

But I think to the lay person or the student or anybody who sees it for the first time, the most shocking bit of the whole procedure is the incision. I always advise my boys the first time they come into theatre not to watch the incision, because that's the sort of thing that if you're a beginner at it, I think you relate it to yourself the first time you see it. Once you're inside, there is no relationship to yourself; you've never seen guts being handled before, so you can't imagine it. But skin being cut is rather more personal.

My work is central to me. I am a vascular surgeon. Full stop. That isn't to say that I don't have lots of other interests, but you couldn't separate me from the vascular surgeon. It's all one really. I love it. I think that's essential; I don't think you could do the sort of work that we do unless you were very whole-heartedly involved and willing to drop things – well, maybe not always terribly willingly, but drop things – to go and put something right if you have to whenever it happens. You can't be half-hearted about it. There are parts of medical practice that are not so immediate. I mean, you can be a dermatologist and not get called out at night ever probably, but in my specialty you have to accept a high emergency load and you have just got to go and do it.

A lot of doctors hate outpatients. Well, I certainly don't. I mean, I actually like sitting down and talking to people and finding out what their problems are. There's intellectual stimulus trying to sort out what their problems are. Suppose you came along and said you were having difficulties with walking, I then ask specific questions: which group of muscles do you get the pain in? when do you get it? is it just after walking? is it easier at night? do you get out of bed with pain? And you build up little bits and pieces until you've got the whole picture and you can then tell what the problem is, usually fairly accurately, just from the story. And then I have the pleasure at the end of it all of doing that which I'm best at, and that's putting it right. I think it's an absolutely superb job because it combines so many nice things.

DR BOB PHILLIPS
RADIOTHERAPIST

I WAS brought up in Gwent in South Wales – Monmouthshire, as it was in those days. My father was in the police force, my uncle, my mother's brother, was a doctor, and his wife was a doctor as well. In fact my brother is a doctor now – he's a G P in Wiltshire and very nicely settled in the country.

From what I had seen, I thought that it was a very worthwhile job, with a lot of human contact and the ability to actually help one's fellow beings. It sounds a bit hack really, but that is how it did come across, from my uncle particularly, who was an exceptionally good doctor. He ran a wonderful practice which I stepped into occasionally when I qualified, and the level of care for his patients was quite extraordinary; it was on a par with the best that I have ever seen. Not only was it his hobby and his life, but it was his total consuming pleasure. He didn't need holidays; he basically gave his patients care around the clock, and would have done it fifty-two weeks of the year if my aunt hadn't put her foot down. I was greatly influenced by him; someone who could get that much satisfaction and pleasure from his work was someone I had to look up to really.

In those days, the competition to work in radiotherapy and oncology, which is the wider treatment of tumours, was not very great; there weren't very many people who wanted to work with cancer patients. That is completely different now. The field has opened up tremendously because there is a much greater interest with the advent of medical treatments of cancer, the expansion in the use of cytotoxic drugs and hormone therapy and all these things.

My first week on the ward I felt very uncomfortable because I just didn't know how to approach patients with cancer. I suppose I had the sort of hang-ups that most people have, and many doctors have, about whether they are able to talk openly to a patient about cancer, and no one had really taught me how to approach patients who were very seriously ill. That sort of thing is actually very difficult to teach, because it is down to the way you are able to communicate with other individuals, and it is actually quite hard to teach someone to draw people out to communicate their inner fears. I well remember my first cancer patient – this lady who had had major problems with cancer over about five years – and thinking, 'My God, what will I say to her?' And I agonized over it, I read her notes again and again, and when I went in behind the curtain, she said, 'You're new.' And when I said, 'Yes', she said, 'Oh, I had better tell you what is wrong with me. I have got cancer in my breast and disease in my bones and lungs, I have had hormone therapy and radiation, and I am really much better and doing very well.' Here was someone who was putting *me* at ease. She realized that I was new and didn't know much about what was going on, and was able to talk very openly about it, and that really helped me enormously.

We do unfortunately see a lot of death, and some of it is lingering. You are staving it off and trying to push it back, but at the end of the day in many of the situations we see, it is inevitable. But on the way, there is an awful lot you can do to improve the quality of patients' lives, albeit for a relatively short time. If they are pain free for the last few weeks of their life, then that is a very positive thing. If they can spend time at home for a few weeks, or if they can make a major event in their lives because you can control symptoms, even though you haven't increased their longevity, then there are tremendous rewards there. You know, time is terribly subjective. Where you and I would say, 'Hell, she has only got three or four weeks to live, why put her through treatment to give her those extra few weeks?' – when you talk with that patient and she says, 'My daughter is getting married in three weeks' time, you have got to get me right,' you can see that even short periods of time can be very important to patients.

In the public's mind, cancer = death: that is it. Some of the chronic debilitating neurological diseases, for example, there is very little that can be done to help, whereas the patients that come to us with cancer, even with some of the most advanced cancers, there is an awful lot that you can do. It may only be in the palliative sense rather than a curative sense, but you can actually improve the quality of their lives enormously.

In fact, the vast majority of cancers, if we can catch them early enough, are curable by one means or another. The problem is that through no fault of the patients, very often, patients present rather late on in the disease, and then the treatment is much more difficult.

Well, there are various things that one has to look out for. Any chronic ulcer or sore that doesn't heal, any bleeding from any of the orifices that is unexplained should be looked at. It may be quite all right, but it is absolutely mandatory to investigate, and you would investigate it with the thought of malignancy in mind until proved otherwise. Any pain that doesn't go away, that is unrelieved, and is causing major functional problems, any swelling or any lump that is unexplained, should be looked at straight away. An unexplained cough that doesn't clear, a hoarseness of the voice. Any abnormal function of the body that doesn't clear with routine treatment or indeed by itself within a reasonable period of time should be investigated. I wouldn't want to frighten people too much, because clearly there are lots of strains and pains and backache and flu and colds and sore throats and all sorts of things that will clear up and not mean anything, but it is when there is an unusually long time course, when things don't get better, or when the symptoms are repeated over a relatively short period of time – these are the things that should be looked at. They may not be significant, but they should be looked at.

There are certain influencing factors, of course. We know that people who have been exposed to asbestos and who are smokers are more likely to get lung cancer. Heavy drinkers and heavy smokers are more likely to get head and neck cancer, lung and laryngeal cancer. So many of the patients that we see who have diseases of the lungs, and around the head, you can almost guarantee that they have been smokers and drinkers. So there are many avoidable cancers, no question as far as I am concerned.

Everyone feels a sense of tremendous guilt and tries to analyse everything that has happened in the light of the possible ways they could have avoided cancer. 'Should I have come earlier?' 'Is there anything else that I could have done?' And most often there is no blame attached, it is just one of those things. It often tears families apart, you know: 'If only we had noticed that dad had this before . . .' 'If only we had brought him earlier.' It is a very potent source of anxiety and distress.

That is a very important aspect of our work in fact; we have to realize that we take on board the rest of the family as well very often, and sometimes that is much more of a problem than the patient, because all the family pressures and all the family problems that may have been there for years suddenly come to the surface, and all the self-recriminations, all the guilt comes out.

I mean, I was in the same position with my mother, who had cervical cancer and has been cured. I had to go down and be told by the consultant that my mother had cancer. So I went down as a specialist in cancer to talk to the consultant. And I sat on the other side of the desk for the first time, and heard someone tell me what was wrong with my mother. I suppose I had all the feelings of shock, because I was pretty sure in my own mind that this was what it would be, but still there was to a certain extent a little hint of unreality about it . . . this couldn't be happening to *my* mother surely? It was quite a chastening and upsetting experience, and I realized then what relatives must go through when they come to see me for information about their loved ones.

With my father, well that was a surprise . . . we didn't expect that. I mean, he came into hospital for something else and the cancer was found, and the operation was more extensive than they thought, and he died about a year later, something like that. They were both extremely good and well adjusted about it, and we were able to talk about the cancer with both of them. With my father, we didn't really talk about dying, that wasn't something that he wanted to or could talk about, but we gave him lots of opportunities to voice his fears and anxieties if he wanted to, and that is what we do to our patients as well.

So often you see patients who are reaching the terminal stages who don't actually want to talk about dying and death. I think the majority of them know what is coming, but they don't want that to be discussed openly. Some people do, but it is not often in my experience. And, of course, many of them have reached by that stage a level of medication for pain where it is actually very difficult for them to hold a rational, reasonable conversation, and therefore the process isn't as distressing as for someone who is bright as a button right up to the end and suddenly dies.

With a lot of the patients, we know that they are going to die, and we try to ease their symptoms and make sure that they don't suffer, but when you know the outcome is going to be inevitable, it is a much more routine, matter of fact thing, if you like. We would have gone through good times, and then difficult times, and more good times probably, and then the final event. There is no doubt that it is rather like losing a member of the family, and we all get upset about it, particularly the junior nurses on the ward who have not seen much of this and their whole aim in life is to help people to get better.

Particularly difficult is when a recurrence develops, when they have been through all the treatment and something else happens. I think that's most difficult of all, coming to terms with that. And that is sometimes a difficult thing for the doctors to come to terms with as well, because you feel then that you have failed. 'Could I have done something different?' And you wonder if you could have done better.

We have to try and alleviate peoples' anxieties, we have to try and build up their morale and try and make them look positively, because as sure as night follows day, there is no future if they can't be positive. That is a lot of our work, to try and encourage people and pick them up when they are down and have really been kicked in the teeth.

When you have been working with cancer patients and working with people who are dying all the time, you do build up barriers, you have to. It can get to you; there are times when you feel, 'My God, it is so awful, why should it happen to him?' But you can't let the sad experiences accumulate and destroy the will to go on and help the many other people who are doing well with treatment. Otherwise you would be dragged under, because one is surrounded by so much tragedy. There are tragic things going on every day in this department, tragic people coming through with the most tragic tales that you wouldn't believe. There was a chap just today who has a sixteen-year-old daughter with cancer of the tongue, which is almost unheard of. A year ago he was in a road traffic accident, they have a child who was born with some sort of congenital abnormality which has caused tremendous problems in bringing him up, he has lost his mother with cancer – all sorts of things, just one after the other, that have happened, and they have been battered and bashed as a family, and now suddenly there is this unbelievable thing happening to them with the sixteen-year-old. All the doctors can't believe it themselves. These are the sorts of things that one does see, so you can imagine that some days you go home and you are emotionally spent, you can't give any more, everything has been drained out of you like a sponge, like somebody has squeezed you out and dropped you down. I'm not kidding you, sometimes you feel that way at the end of the day.

You see so much courage, raw courage, People talk about courageous acts in sport and all this sort of thing, but my God, you see some amazing characters who are just fighting their disease and have come to terms with it. You feel almost insignificant beside the strength and faith and courage of particular individuals, and in total awe of that sort of spirit, and I often think, 'Christ, if I had a disease like that, my face would be to the wall months ago.'

There is a certain formality about the relationship between the doctor and the patient which is sometimes difficult to get over, and the patient will not necessarily unload everything to you, but when the nurse is there making the bed or bathing them or combing their hair or giving them an injection, they will say, 'Well, I'm really worried about dying', or 'How long do you think that I have got?' Now, they may not do that to me, but the nurse is there with them all the time, and there are all sorts of things that they will ask her because it is a much more informal relationship, so it is much easier for them to unload their fears. And this is where Mandy, the sister,* is so brilliant, because she takes all this on board, and she tells us what the patients say to her and what the real problems are with the patients and their families. And that way it makes our job a lot easier; it's very much a team effort.

People put doctors on pedestals and there is an aura surrounding us, and it is very easy to become completely consumed with one's own self-importance. Because people come to my room, to any doctor's room, and actually unload everything, the sorts of things that you probably wouldn't tell your best friend or your wife or husband, and they will take almost as gospel what you say, so it is very easy to become complacent and arrogant, I think. And because some of us are making life and death decisions, and what we say may have an absolutely crucial impact on a fellow human being, it is a situation where you can feel very important. You should be brought down to earth. Bang!

Well I'll tell you, if you really analysed what you were doing, you would be the most humble person on God's earth. The mistakes that we make, the errors, I don't mean fatal mistakes, but I mean little things where you have not diagnosed something perhaps as soon as you should, or have got something a little bit wrong. The whole time if you really analyse your own perform-ance you can find ways in which you should improve.

*Mandy Smith, see p. 181.

PROFESSOR DAVID POSWILLO

ORAL AND MAXILLA SURGEON

Do you know that one person in fifty is born malformed, all told? And 70 per cent of malformations occur in the head and neck? Club foot, cleft lip and palate, and spina bifida are the three most common malformations. Harelip and cleft palate are frequently combined, occurring about once in 700 births, and after spina bifida, it's probably the most common malformation.

Some of the worst malformations are absolutely horrifying: for example, where large areas of the brain have developed outside the skull, and the whole face is split into two; sometimes a strip of the amnion, the lining of the womb, comes loose and gets swallowed into the mouth of the foetus, and then it just tears its way through the face and the eye and out through the skull, and the whole skull is split apart when they're born; or the amnion may strangle itself around an arm and amputate a hand or leg, and these are pretty horrifying things, especially if the baby is born and the leg comes out as a separate entity, unattached to the body.

You don't see these deformities in the streets because one doesn't defer operating on these horrifying things. Quite a lot of them go into sheltered environments, like Chailey in Sussex, and they're cared for and looked after there by specialists who can gradually get them reconstructed and into a condition to go back into society.

Man either hates or adores the malformed. I have a collection of terracotta carvings and facial masks which go back to about 800 BC which depict a condition called hemifacial microsomia, where one half of the face doesn't develop normally, and in South America they tended to revere these people as gods and worship them, and a number of civilizations tended to promote these people to leaders of the tribe because of their unique facial appearance.

The animal kingdom automatically destroys the malformed; they instinctively know when an offspring is malformed, even if they only have a cleft in the palate which they can't observe. And that makes it very difficult doing experimental work with malformation in animals.

My whole academic life interest has been looking at the mechanisms of deformity and trying to establish how many mechanisms there may be, and we really have only a fairly superficial knowledge in many of these things. I myself haven't done all that well. I've discovered about three or four, but there are many, many more that I don't know about, and some of the mechanisms that I've delineated may be secondary or tertiary, they may not be the primary event.

One of the mechanisms that I've looked at is what's called a postural malformation mechanism, where there's a spontaneous loss of amniotic fluid which compresses the developing embryo in the womb into an unusual position, jams the head against the chest, say, or wedges the tongue in between the palatal shelves, and you get cleft palate, underdeveloped chin, you sometimes get a club foot, and congenital deformation of the hip.

Then there are two other mechanisms that I've identified which cause quite unusual facial deformity. In hemifacial microsomal condition, that condition depicted in my terracotta carvings, I've established that a haemorrhage occurs at about day thirty-five to forty of embryonic development, and spreads into the tissue and destroys a lot of developing tissues, which then can't grow.

And the third one I discovered is related to how thalidomide works. There are very specialized cells that develop in the midbrain at about day twenty of development, and many of these cells migrate out to the developing face and other parts of the body, and agents such as thalidomide and acutane, a vitamin A compound that's causing a lot of malformation in America, can kill off these highly specialized cells. You can equate it with not having sufficient bricks and mortar with which to build the basic foundations, and therefore nature has to effect a compromise, and it does its best with the cells that it's got there, but you get a greatly diminished facial structure, and so you get clefts, bones fail to develop properly, and all sorts of other abnormalities.

Deformity has a genetic background, but there are probably multiple factors in our environment, some of them things like alcohol and smoking, or taking analgesics in the early stages of pregnancy, and all of these pile up on top of a genetic predisposition and push the threshold towards malformation. This is much more common in social classes four and five, probably because you find more smoking and drinking in those groups.

Some of the patients come back to you and ask what they should do about having families. Well, the geneticists have worked out good risk tables for us; if it's an autosomal dominant genetic thing, where it comes down in the family line, you know generally speaking that the risk factor is that one or two of their offspring are going to be malformed. If it's a severe cleft of the lip and palate, you know that there's a 10 or 15 per cent risk of the offspring being malformed; if it's just a simple unilateral cleft, the risk is about 4 per cent.

I think molecular biology is going to help us identify a large number of mechanisms, although I'm not sure it will tell us precisely what the initiating factors are. If we take cancer as an example, we know that cells misbehave in cancer, and we know that quite a lot of cancerous cells can be handled perfectly reasonably by the body, which will just destroy them and they will disappear. But there are situations in which the body's defence mechanisms fail, and the cancer can proceed and develop; what we've got to do is get down to the fundamental flaw in the cell which starts dividing regardless of what's going on around it, and that's going to be the molecular biologist's job without question.

We're in the middle of an absolute revolution in medical management. We can't quite see it yet, but I think that people will look on this age as being the turning point in medical progress.

For one thing, we will have revolutionary changes in the management of disease, away from major intervention and much more towards non-interventional control, for instance, learning to control disease by non-invasive techniques. We're seeing it happen now already. Whereas once upon a time gallstones were taken out by direct surgical removal, now they use lithotriptors, which fragment them up and pulverize them, and they're then just spontaneously passed out of the system. And the same for kidney stones and bladder stones. We now have ways of passing catheters into malformed blood vessels and repairing them and doing things of this kind.

I mean, it's just as big a leap as when we discovered antibiotics. We're on the point of quantum leaps now.

DR RAY POWLES
LEUKAEMIOLOGIST

Of course I question why people get leukaemia. And the answer to that is inescapable – which is the fact that basically life is a sod. You can't back out of that. In the early part of the year, in one week, I had two mothers in their late twenties die leaving six children under the age of six. Now, the only way you can look at that is life is a sod. But it doesn't mean to say that you have to go under, and that is one of the reasons why I try to create within the unit a feeling of optimism, happiness, joking.

Death never gets better, it doesn't get any easier. You lose a bit every time. I had a patient last Friday die absolutely unexpectedly at home. He had been discharged from hospital the day before. He had a massive haemoptysis, coughed up several pints of blood and died within half an hour. So on Monday morning at 8 a.m. I had to go to the coroner's post-mortem at Epsom mortuary. And there was this guy whom I had known well over the previous month and thought that I was well on the way to helping – got him into remission and so on – and I had to go and see him spread open end to end, top of his head off, brain out, and go through the organs looking to see what caused it. Now, if you know the guy and had been joking with him two days before, and you are then seeing him on the table, you cannot cope with that by ignoring it or laughing it off. Of course you lose a bit every time. I think if you don't, in our business, you want for out.

I got TB just after I left school and spent seven months in hospital. I went from being absolutely fit one day to having a haemorrhage and being in a TB hospital surrounded by TB patients, and at least two patients died in that ward while I was there.

Actually, it was quite good to have been a patient and to have been really quite ill, and that definitely gave me a great insight into being on the receiving end, which I don't think I have ever lost.

Leukaemia is cancer of the blood, but it's really of the bone marrow, because your blood comes from your bone marrow.

Well, first of all, there is nothing special about people who get leukaemia, they are absolutely ordinary. The first symptoms are very ordinary too, very general practice Monday morning type thing; a GP would have thirty of those sitting outside, but he will see one leukaemia a year. Basically you feel like you have got flu, you are pale because you're anaemic, and you often have got some bruising – but then, everyone has got some bruising. What happens next is that the GP sees that patient with the twenty-nine others, throws some antibiotics at them and sends them all home. Two days later the leukaemia chap comes back feeling bloody ill. GPs are extremely good at spotting who is ill and who is not; they take one look at this person, still with no idea what is wrong, and shunt him off to hospital for a blood test. And if it is leukaemia, the GP may feel guilty about it, and the family often say, 'Why didn't the GP send him two days prior?' But that is totally unfair, I am so sympathetic to the GPs on this basis, which is that the symptoms of leukaemia are everyday, common, ordinary problems.

Leukaemia is relatively rare, about five people per 100,000 per year get it, so in Britain you'd be talking between 5,000 and 11,000 new cases a year, of which almost all will die. But perhaps the reason it is such a well-known disease is because it affects young people, children particularly, and it has had great publicity through things like successful bone marrow transplantation (modest success, because we are still a long way from wiping out leukaemia), but the thing is there are groups of patients with leukaemia now that we can definitely cure and give a normal life expectancy to.

The young ones, people under the age of fifty, we can offer a 50 per cent chance of cure. And there are some childhood leukaemia, particularly in girls, where we can offer an 80 per cent chance of cure. Leukaemia gets more and more common as you get older; after seventy, we don't even attempt to cure it: we treat it, we control it, we palliate, we can get patients back to a normal life, sometimes for quite long periods, but sooner or later all of them are going to die of the disease.

Before 1947 there were no effective drug treatments for cancer, but when chemotherapy and a whole group of drugs became available from the mid-fifties onwards, one began to see results, and there were some patients that were definitely being benefited and even some people who were being cured. Leukaemia was the first of the cancers to respond to chemotherapy and drug treatment, and since then it has led the way in most of the cancer treatment developments, partly because it is a disease that is relatively simple to assess and measure – you can easily measure things in blood and marrow. The trouble with most cancers is that they are at some stages such small lumps and bumps you can't detect the damn things, even though inevitably they are going to come back bigger.

Now, as soon as it became apparent that giving drugs could cure some cancers and control many, there had to be a group of doctors that were going to do that. And what is happening now more and more is that we are trying to bring cancer together as a specialty in its own right, and the expansion of the specialist has been a feature of what's been happening in the health service. There are new disciplines like medical oncology, which is what I am, that didn't exist twenty years ago. It just so happens, for example, that my twin brother specializes in breast cancer, solely breast cancer, sees nothing else. I only see leukaemia. We have even become specialized within a specialty, so I would no more know how to treat lung cancer, say, than to fly. And if you look at the jobs being advertised in the *BMJ*, I doubt whether there is a single advertisement for a consultant in general medicine; if it is general medicine, it will always be with a specialist interest in something.

Well, there are really only two major cancer hospitals in Britain – that's us, the Royal Marsden, and the Christie Institute in Manchester – and then there is another famous cancer hospital, the Sloane–Kettering, in New York.

We only think cancer here, which has got to be a plus. We don't take undergraduates. All our teaching is at a very much higher level; we're teaching people who are already specialists in cancer. And because all the patients here are cancer, and our back-up systems are oriented just to cancer patients, it means we have a dedication to cancer that gives us a wider expertise than you'd ever get in a general hospital.

I run a specialist ward of sixteen beds and the people in that ward are intimately linked with research programmes that we have on-going. There are some very important factors when we are picking patients for the sixteen beds. Age is very important. I don't see patients over the age of fifty. Number two, preferably not treated previously by other people, so you are not picking up a dog's dinner. Number three, the disease sub-type. The commonest leukaemia and the one I'm most interested in is called acute myeloblastic leukaemia, but it is also the biggest challenge. Until fifteen years ago it was universally fatal. Now, if you are a young patient and have a suitable brother or sister as a bone marrow donor, we can cure over 50 per cent – and that is a major development. So if I have got one bed and somebody says that they have got a seventy-four-year-old chronic lymphatic, and someone else offers me a sixteen-year-acute myeloblastic with four brothers and sisters, then it is very easy for me to decide which one of those I will take. Now, the seventy-four-year-old might be pretty pissed off, here is a chance waiting for him, all the expertise that we have got; but he is not going to come here because we can't learn enough from him. I am being very selective.

I make it sound as if they're guinea pigs, but they profit by it as it so happens. First of all they have someone such as me who has spent twenty years only treating leukaemia. I am not fogged up or muddled by other outside influences; I don't have to worry about another clinic tomorrow; my only interest is leukaemia. I know arguably more about leukaemia than any other people worldwide. The second thing is that the patient is going to profit because the cash input of my unit will be three times anywhere else. I have got thirty-four nurses to cover sixteen beds. Thirty-four trained, qualified, highly dedicated nurses. I have got a whole team of seventy-four people. I can bring in ancillary people that are again specialized, for instance my social worker only looks after leukaemia, and there is no other social worker in Britain that only looks after leukaemia.

I have got a very approachable set-up. We don't have any visiting-time restrictions, and I think having an informal, easy-going, happyish sort of environment definitely helps. I hope that I have been a force in breaking down many dogmas and stigmas. For example, all the patients call me Ray. I wear jeans and sports shirts. Calling the doctor by his surname, the second you do that, you put up a barrier; there's too much of that in hospitals. White coat and stethoscope, formal ward rounds where the patients have to lie in bed rigid to attention while the consultant and all his junior staff come round with the students and so on. All these things are setting up barriers – us and them – and you have got to get rid of those.

If you have a close organization, then of course you develop a close relationship with the patients emotionally. This applies more to the nurses than the doctors; nurses burn out at about two to three years, and the senior sisters, very few of them last longer than four years.

But I'm stuck here. I have got a job to do. I think for me one of the things that compensates for the difficulty of dealing emotionally with people who die and that you know well and are fond of is the fact that you do have some purpose at the end of it. I am actually trying to cure leukaemia. I'll give an analogy: you and I get into a loop the loop aeroplane together; if I'm flying the thing, it is less likely that I am going to be sick than you, although we are both going through the same thing. And that is, I suppose, the nearest reason to why I can resist the emotional burn-out easier than the nurses can.

I can tell when somebody is going to die, anything from one to fourteen days before. I can look at them from the end of the bed and say, 'This person is dying.' You can't say exactly when they are going to die, but what you are saying is that a process has started in this person where they are going down a physiological pathway of death. It is like I'm looking at those trees out my window there, and I know that early autumn is starting, although the leaves haven't gone yellow and haven't fallen off.

People ask why we can't cure cancer when we can send people into space. Well, the moon is bloody easy. The body has spent a million years developing under its own steam and one has got to try and unravel that extraordinarily complicated pathway where nobody has left you the blue prints, and even if they had we would still find it unbelievable. If every person in this world was working full-time on the project, to give you some idea of the dimensions as I see it, I don't believe in twenty years' time we would get anywhere nearer understanding the half of the body. And if you get into the whole area of the process of thinking, how does a thought make a muscle work? how does a thought produce a chemical? . . . once you get into that area, coming back to the space analogy, we are trying to send a man to the stars in the steam age.

If I thought we knew one-tenth about leukaemia I would think that we had done bloody well. We may know a very useful 10 per cent, but I have a feeling that if I sat my colleagues around the table and put up an argument as to why it was only, say, 1 per cent, we would walk away from that table saying that we know 1 per cent. It is depressing, you know.

I will not deny the fact that leukaemia is an emotive word. I talk a lot to the media, television, people like you, and I am aware by doing that I get government backing, because they back what they hear about. When Ian Botham walked from John O'Groats to Land's End, he turned leukaemia for a month into a household

154 · THE NOBLE TRADITION

word. And I think that leukaemia as a word is better known now on the street than it was twenty years ago. They don't know what it is necessarily, but they know that it involves young people and children and is horrible.

Well, I am very lucky because this hospital is a modern hospital in large grounds with an enormous research institute, wonderful ward and nursing to staff ratio, a budget three times anybody else's, and I can say that this has got to be the National Health Service at its best. So there is no way that I could criticize the Health Service at all. But I know, of the people that you will see, you will find very few who will say what I have just said.

DR RUSSELL REID

TRANSEXUAL SPECIALIST

———

M Y special interest, which I'm fascinated by, is in that particular, very rare category of sexual disorders to do with one's identity: sexual dysphoria, which is an unhappiness with one's sense of masculinity or femininity.

A transexual is a person whose biological sex is out of step with their psychological sex; in other words, they feel they're women who have men's bodies, or they feel they're men who have women's bodies. The cliché is, 'I'm a man trapped in a woman's body.'

I tend to see about five to seven new transexuals a week, and have done for the last two or three years, referred by other doctors all over the country and occasionally from Europe.

For example, last night I saw a man who had run a cycle firm for many years. He came dressed as a woman, despite the fact that he had a rather masculine look about him and he obviously shaves. He had make-up on, and rather large talon-like nails over his fingernails. He dated his problem back many years. He said that in the Army he had once been mistaken for a woman over the telephone, and also, he said, he felt his endurance was such that he couldn't be a man because he couldn't cycle more than seventy miles. It seemed a strange rationalization. He also felt that his body was rather flabby and feminine-looking, and in fact it was, and all of these things added together to make him believe that he was a woman. He said something a lot of people in his position say: 'As a man my life is dreadful. I'm lonely, I don't get on with people, I'm aggressive and rather unpleasant –

but I have to be like that to run my business and survive. But coming home in the evening, I put on a frock or a skirt and it changes me into a gentle, soft person, and I like myself as a woman, I can relax in that role, I feel happy about myself.'

That's a very common scenario in fact. The transexual population would desperately like to think that there was something biological or physical going on. They all want blood tests to check their hormone levels and their chromosomes. They all think, 'If only we could *prove* that I'm genuine, that I'm really a woman in a man's body.' But when they have a test, invariably they're a normal biological man.

The salient points are that it's almost as if these people have two personalities, a male and a female persona. They opt for one and reject the other. For instance, they dislike their own male bodies, particularly their genitals, they don't like the idea of getting erections and ejaculating, they like being with women, they like the idea of coming across as a woman, they like all the feminine mannerisms.

Diagnostically, my label would be that here's a transvestite progressing towards transexualism. I mean, he's episodically transvestite, he's not living full-time as a woman. Many of them spend years with the double life, compartmentalizing, spending the evenings and weekends as a woman, which they prefer, but having to support wife and kids and keep a business going as a man.

At this point it's a psychological state. I mean, the physiological things that follow, like the hormone changes and surgery, are induced from outside. He becomes a transexual when he starts living exclusively as a woman and wants to emulate a woman in every way, and is heading towards surgery to get rid of his male genitals.

The females who want to be males typically have had a compulsion, a determination, to live their lives as men. They'll have a pretty classical background of childhood tomboyism, they hate wearing skirts, they play with the boys in rough and tumble games, they're sexually attracted to girls, they hate having periods, they hate having breasts. They end up at a gender clinic where they'll be given masculinizing hormones, such as testosterone, an oily solution which you draw out with great difficulty into a 2-ml syringe and inject deep into the muscles of the buttocks. It's injected once a month usually, and it suppresses the periods, although it doesn't stop the breasts, which have to be removed surgically.

It occasionally causes balding, occasionally acne, an increase in weight, increased muscle bulk, beard growth, lowering of the voice, suppression of periods, usually increased strength and often increased libido; their clitoris enlarges, and they usually feel more assertive and more aggressive. Some of them get into trouble with that as a complication actually, they become prone to losing their temper and throwing tantrums.

For men changing to women, hormone arrangements are a bit more complicated, and the effects are more subtle. The first thing that happens is that they're rendered impotent, and it becomes harder for them to get erections and ejaculate. The second thing that happens is their breasts start enlarging slowly, and swelling, and tingling. The third thing that happens is the psychological effects; they say that they become more easily turned to tears, more emotional – who knows whether that's true – I think that's a placebo effect possibly.

I don't want to brag, but usually you can tell within a few minutes of them walking in the door and sitting down whether they're genuine or not. People don't come along on a whim saying, 'I want to be a lady. I want to change my sex' – although occasionally people have had gender dysphoric feelings as a symptom of depression, and if you rush in and do too much too soon, and the depression lifts and they change their mind, you're in hot water.

They must decide for themselves really whether what they're doing is correct for themselves. Both sexes have to show that they're successful in their chosen role for at least a year, and that includes being self-supporting and emotionally stable, and that they've adjusted socially before they're given anything as irreversible as surgery. There are various criteria laid down by an organization established in America called the Harry Benjaman Gender Dysphoria Association, and they have guidelines and principles of treatment which require two doctors with a specialist interest in gender to give the O K before any surgery is done.

These operations are surprisingly successful. 80 per cent do really very well according to the follow-up studies after the operation. Many of them don't have an awful lot of trouble changing over and fitting in. Remember, the men were often rather feminine and the females rather male. Usually the ones with partners and the ones who get into a stable relationship do better. But the statistics are quite hard to get because these people go away and they don't like to come back to doctors and hospitals and psychiatrists. They want to put the past behind them and they blend into the suburban housewife scene and many of them are never heard of again.

Britain provides a very bare minimum for care for these people. Mind you, having said that, there are patients from all over Europe who come to England for the operation because of the surgeons, and one particular surgeon in London is the best surgeon in the country, and he's got a very good reputation for doing a very good operation in terms of cosmetic appearance, function, depth and lack of complications afterwards.

While we're on that subject, I should mention that the new vagina is fashioned from the skin of the penis or scrotum, so sensation is still there, including the ability to experience orgasm during masturbation or sex activities.

Making a penis for women is called feloplastisurgery. It isn't done very often, it's very experimental still. It's a three- or four-stage procedure to create a penis from a tube of skin either on the thigh or abdomen. Unfortunately, it's not functional in terms of being used as a sex organ, or to urinate standing, and there are various other devices being thought out at the present time to try and make a better job of this feloplasty procedure. It's really prescribed more as a 'pants filler', it fills their pants and that's really all they can expect. One of the things they have been doing is to free up the clitoris, fuse the labia and put in artificial testes, so it looks like a miniature penis and scrotum, but technically it's rather a difficult procedure. You can remove breasts quite success-fully, although there are scars; you can augment breasts for male to females; you can do cosmetic operations on the face . . . but you can't make a very good penis.

To be honest, this sort of work makes my life more interesting. I find these people absolutely fascinating. Here are people with a passion. People with a huge problem which they are doing something about, and the hurdles and obstacles that they over-come make your or my problems pale into insignificance. I believe that these people are hurting more than most other of my walking well – you know, my neurotic, unhappy, bored, relatively affluent housewives from the suburbs that I see in my general psychiatric work. I mean, these are very courageous people and I respect them immensely, and I'm absolutely intrigued by the subject. My life would be dull and boring if I were dealing with just schizophrenics in this hospital.

So that's why I like it; I find it fascinating. I find anything to do with sexual identity and behaviour really of great interest, and I would be miserable if I had to give my gender work up.

DR PATRICIA SARTOREY

PAEDIATRICIAN

WHILE I was doing an English degree at university, I couldn't decide what to do afterwards, and I had a sort of crisis and got very depressed. And then one night I had a dream that I was going to do medicine and when I woke up I actually seriously started to think about it. And I thought that medicine had enough of a mix of humanity and science and academia to be appealing, and doing something that was related to people and caring – and not money orientated – which is what a lot of my contemporaries at Oxford were into. So I don't know, the reasons that you stay in it are different from the reasons you start, and the whole thing evolves.

My parents are Italian. They both came from an obscure rural village and they emigrated here in the early fifties. My father works in a factory and I went to a direct grant school and then did my English degree at Oxford, and eventually I went to Guy's and trained there.

So I started medicine as a mature student. I was only twenty-one, but I was older than the people there who had just done 'A' levels. Eighteen-year-olds starting medicine do seem terribly young. In fact, it is a bit alarming because I don't know that they have time to get on with just growing up when they are at medical school, because they are so hard-worked. I mean, it is very easy to get channelled at fifteen into science 'A' levels and medicine and so on, and really have little time to look outside that.

I enjoyed paeds and psychiatry most as a student. It wasn't as pompous as adult medicine. I think on the whole paediatricians are more open and communicative and liberal in their general outlook, because you have to be more open and communicative in paediatrics than you have to be in medicine. You can be a successful adult physician and never tell your patient the truth and not believe in their right to know, whereas in paeds, because you are forced to seek the parents' cooperation, you have to divulge information, and you really have to recognize their right to have it. And I think on the whole it is difficult to be pompous on a ward round if there is a toddler pushing a train in between your feet, and you do find paediatricians will suddenly sit down and start playing with a child, or look at a baby in the middle of a discussion and say, 'Isn't he nice!' I think that is quite 'paediatric'. That openness appealed to me and just the children themselves are much more fun.

This is a very nice hospital, very friendly and welcoming environment, I think parents like it. It *is* messy – children's hospitals are always messy. There are parents and babies and toys littered around; there are no nice neat regimented wards with all the sheets made up in a particular way because that is how sister likes them, and ward rounds aren't accompanied by a total hushed silence in the rest of the ward, like with some of the physicians that I trained under. You can't do that in paediatrics; there is always background noise, things going on, children's meals and children's games and so on, so the atmosphere is much more homely.

The patient role isn't so alien for a child. I mean, with an adult you completely take away all the things that define them as a person when you put them in hospital: you take away their job, you take away their family role, they are not in their normal clothes, or doing any of the things they normally would do. You are no longer a husband or father, you are just a sick old man in pyjamas stuck in bed. Whereas with a child who's dependent upon his or her parents and spends his time playing or at school – in hospital their parents are there, so it is the same care givers with the nurses and doctors adding to that. If they are well enough, they go to school or they run around and play, so although the environment is slightly different, I don't think their personality is disrupted nearly as much, particularly now that parents can stay. There must be very few paediatric units where that can't happen. Most children's hospitals have somewhere where parents can sleep; they either have a parent's unit with bedrooms or, if they want to stay by the child, we have a whole variety of couches and camp beds and sofas that are set up in the ward in between the beds. Sometimes it can get extremely crowded, but we never turn a parent away. They're crammed in, they sleep in the bathroom, the day room, the waiting room, anywhere where there is room.

I think the children often don't realize I am a doctor. Children have an image of doctors wearing white coats, and most of the physicians at the Children's Hospital don't wear coats. I usually say that I am Doctor Pat, because then they can relate it with Postman Pat. They see you as a sort of mixture of playmate, friend and monster, and they distinguish between the times when you are being a friend and when, say, you are going to take blood. They don't hold it against you, but they know when you go in every morning at 8.30 a.m. to do a blood test that they are not going to like that. There is one little boy I remember, little Danvers, who was two and a half, and every time that I went in to do his blood test he would say, 'Lady, lady, leave my hand, lady!' And I would take the blood, and he would be upset, but then half an hour later I would come back to examine him to look at his ears and his eyes and his tummy, and he was great, he loved being examined. He would hold his ears and then he would take the oroscope and say, 'Me look teddy's ears', and it was a game and his eyes would light up when I walked in.

When children are very ill they don't talk very much and they moan. But on the whole they show enormous resilience, and if you can get them over the dreadful acute illness bit, they do perk up quite quickly, much more quickly than adults. You can see incredible changes. They can go downhill very quickly, but they come back uphill very quickly as well.

Most children's deaths happen in hospital, so one does tend to see a bit. If you are seventy-five, you expect to die; it is not outrageous for an old person to die. But it is outrageous for a baby to die, or a child of five or ten, because they have still got their whole lives in front of them. It is always very upsetting.

Every general paediatrician has to do both general paediatrics and neonates. That's an important part of paediatrics. A lady goes into labour at twenty-eight weeks and a paediatric team is there ready to resuscitate the baby and get it stabilized and transfer it to a special care baby unit, and then treat whatever problems arise.

Premature babies are red and shiny and very small – they look like skinned rabbits! If they are very premature, before twenty-four weeks, then the eyelids are fused, and that is actually a sign that they may not do terribly well. But they have everything: they have all their fingers, all their limbs are perfectly formed, they have all their organs, their face is normal, the brain is a normal structure, they have hair, they have nails, there isn't anything missing, but it is all very small and immature. They have got everything, but are just not ready to function in the outside world.

The newspapers always talk about them 'weighing less than a bag of sugar', just to give people some idea about how much they weigh. That's a bit of a joke for us, because that is not quite how we perceive it. The other paediatric joke is when newspapers talk in clichés: '. . . This tiny baby in the incubator, fighting for his life' – more often than not the baby is desperately trying to die. *They* are not fighting for their lives – *we* are doing the fighting.

It is not just the lungs that won't work. They have also got very delicate brains, so they risk having a haemorrhage inside the brain, an intracranial haemorrhage, which can cause significant handicap later as a result. They can't digest food because their gut isn't mature, so you have to give them fluids via a vein. You have to think about every function because their defence systems haven't developed yet. Their kidneys aren't as mature as an older baby's so they can run into problems with fluids and salt and so on. There are just so many organs that can misfunction.

I would like to have more time to do hundreds of other things, but one of the problems about medicine, and I suppose paediatrics particularly, is that it is very demanding in terms of time, and it doesn't leave much space for anything else. Because if you are spending however many hours a week actually physically working and a few more hours reading journals, and then you have to sleep and eat, and go out a few times, that's it, there is no more time left to do anything else, certainly as a junior doctor. So you have to hold your interests in abeyance and keep them for when there is a bit more time. Although of course there's never more time. Retirement!

I don't think that work should be the only definition of oneself, but I think even before I wanted to do medicine I always saw myself as being defined in terms of my job, I expected to work, I didn't expect to be a housewife. Well, there are times when I resent it, but there isn't anything else that I would rather do. I would rather define myself in terms of what my work is than in terms of my hobbies. I mean, if you are an accountant but the main interest in your life is horse-racing, then being an accountant is peripheral, it is just a money churner. And I think my decision to do medicine was partly to do with choosing a profession that would be worthy of defining one's life or a major part of it, and wouldn't be a peripheral thing.

The fact is that in a capitalist society, particularly a Thatcherite society, people are valued if they make money, and jobs are valued if they are to do with money, more than if you do something 'menial' like looking after sick children, or teaching children or whatever. Status is all in terms of making wealth with very little care for what life is really about.

Money is just a means to an end, but it has become an end in itself, and that reflects in things like people with whom I was at university who went into merchant banking and now earn three or four times as much as I do, and they've got bigger cars and vast houses in London and so on. I'm sure that I work as hard in terms of hours, but it is just not as valued. I mean, I *am* quite satisfied with the pay as it is, but it just shows how society values what people do.

I think it's scandalous that wards are closing because there aren't enough nurses because they aren't paid enough to want to stay in nursing after they're trained. The fact that authorities will say to a department, like they did last year to the Guy's cardiology department, 'Right, you have done all the heart operations on children you are allowed this year, any more children that come after the end of this month will just have to lump it', I think that is criminal, because life is about living, it is not about money, and you can't possibly make something like the NHS pay. I mean, it is not a money-making venture; you haven't got a product at the end of it. Health doesn't generate wealth, it just generates health, which is what life is about. You can't live without life or health, and yet it is just not valued.

There are times when you can't find a bed for an under-one anywhere in Birmingham. It makes me very afraid that before the winter is out there are going to be children dying because there is nowhere for them to go. And I think that is entirely the fault of the whole way that we have come to see priorities. They are spending money on bombs instead of hospitals, which I think is completely negative and destructive.

That's my spiel on politics! You've probably heard it millions of times before. But I think politics is central to medicine. I went into medicine for partly political reasons – the point of going into something that is to do with people and caring rather than to do with money is basically political.

I also do community child health in Nechells, which is a

suburb of Birmingham, and I see an enormous number of problems.

There are children on the 'at risk' register, where mum is really unable to cope. She may love her children, but really has little idea how to look after them, how much to feed them, how to bring them up or deal with behaviour problems, and maybe she whacks them when she loses her temper. It's not necessarily lack of love, just lack of knowing what to do or how to do it. The children tend to be small and slightly undernourished, their development is often delayed because they are not stimulated at home, they're not given anything to do, just plonked in front of the telly. And they are behind with their speech and are dressed in ragged tatty clothes and are a bit dirty, and they are susceptible to chest infections and ear infections. You get families like that everywhere, but there are more of them in places like Nechells.

Inner-city Birmingham is grotty, but Nechells is the grottiest. There has recently been a survey of health in the city, looking at the various parameters like uptake of services and adult mortality and morbidity figures, and Nechells has come out worse for nearly all of them.

The social circumstances there are bad. There are a lot of high-rise flats, graffiti over the stairs, and people who wee in the corridors, and a lot of very poor unemployed single parents, who are themselves the product of single-parent families. It is a very limited and brutalizing environment to grow up in, and with gang fights going on all the time outside, it is a culture into which it is very easy for them to get drawn. I mean, the whole cycle goes on and on, and I can see the children that I am looking after in twenty years being parents of the next lot of very deprived, developmentally delayed, undernourished, pale, inner-city children.

You can't deal with housing or unemployment or poverty as a doctor; you can only deal with its effects and try to alleviate it.

I would say that you can break out of it if you happen to be bright and lucky and fairly determined, but a lot of people aren't, and it isn't their fault. That is a very Thatcherist idea, leaving those who can't do it for themselves where they are and not helping. It implies a sort of moral judgement on them for not being able to help themselves.

DAME CICELY SAUNDERS

HOSPICE DIRECTOR

───

It was because of the war that a friend's sister had started nursing, and I suddenly thought, 'Good Heavens, that is what I want to do, and that is what I am going to do.' So I persuaded my parents to let me nurse, and I absolutely loved it, and it was the first time in my life that I felt happy.

A lot of what we were doing was looking after soldiers and sailors because St Thomas's was out in the sector, and I didn't happen to be on duty when a patient died in the ward until I had been nursing nearly a year. But I very quickly got interested in patients with cancer – I had a particular feeling for cancer patients – and so when I started doing my practical training, I chose to go to what was then called the Royal Cancer Hospital, and later became the Marsden, and the moment I was there, I knew that these were my people and this is what I had to do.

I remember going to visit a patient at home. I got there too late and she had already gone, but the door was still ajar and I went in. And there was this awful smell of loneliness and desolation, and it impelled me to do something about this.

We didn't have anti-cancer drugs in those days; we had surgery and radiotherapy. There was a very negative attitude towards the control of pain which I instinctively felt was wrong. Attitude to pain was very much what I'm afraid you sometimes still meet: acute pain is an event, and you give something for it and wait for the patient to have pain again before you give it again. But you want to use your drugs to prevent pain ever happening, because constant pain needs constant control.

Our belief encodes looking at what one would refer to as a kind of total pain – physical, social, mental, emotional and spiritual – because pain is a whole experience. When somebody says to you, 'It is all pain', they are not only talking about their physical pain; they are talking about their loss of independence, they are talking about their worries about their family, they are talking about their search for meaning in their lives, they are talking about feeling depressed, isolated, and all the other things.

Well, we were the first hospice that set out to take the academic model of research and teaching and put it into the field of care of the dying, in particular those dying of pain of cancer.

And to care for dying people is to welcome them; hospice is a very good name for hospitality. We welcome them as themselves and say to them, 'We will try and see what we can do to help, but the important thing is you as yourself, as part of your family, your inner needs and wishes, and we will do all we can to help you to live up until you die, and your family to live on afterwards.'

Death remains a mystery, and when you are with somebody at the moment in which the last breath is taken, even if they have been unconscious before, there is a difference. Often one sees the spirit get stronger in terms of endurance, because in crisis we move fast: in terms of reconciliation, in terms of living a lifetime in three weeks, as you come up to the crisis of dying, people can sort out rotten old family problems that have been hanging about for years. I have seen so many times the spirit becomes stronger as the body becomes weaker that it is impossible to see an ending at the moment of death, quite apart from the fact that as a Christian I don't believe that this is the end.

Death can be seen in a positive way, but I am not detracting from the anguish of parting. What is difficult is when you hear that crying the moment that somebody dies, which is different in quality from any other times, and you see the anguish of parting. I know something about the awful emptiness of bereavement, and that comes back to you.

I'm not scared of dying, except obviously it is a mystery and I don't have too much confidence that I am necessarily going to do terribly well myself. I'll wait and see. You don't get strength until you have got to the day.

I am much more frightened of my husband's death than I am of my own. My husband was awfully frail and ill and I battled him through difficult things each one of the last three years. I mean, he was eighty-seven in February, and he is still painting; he was doing a portrait this morning.

It is not a leper colony on our wards, it is not a death camp. But it does have tragedies. A girl of thirty-seven died here in the early hours of Sunday morning leaving three kids, the youngest of whom was four and a half, who knew very little about how ill his mother was, though the five- and seven-year-olds did appreciate it. If only she had come to see us a week or two sooner, we know that we could have created an atmosphere in which that family could have done more about finding its own strength and saying goodbye and being able to move on.

I see that you find this upsetting, but do I look depressed? We are meeting people who are showing courage and endurance and so often coping . . . the human capacity for coping! It is much better than meeting superficial and materialistic people who are all busy with getting and spending.

We have got confidence in ourselves because we have really worked hard over these twenty years, driven ourselves to be better and better at controlling symptoms and understanding families. We also get confidence from the patient because when they come in we know that look of pain will go off their faces, and we know that we will very likely do something special with this patient. We get the most marvellous letters continually back from families.

The money situation is dire! We have lived off faith and an overdraft all the time, and our overdraft is horrid. Just over one-third of our support comes from the National Health Service and all the rest is gifts and grants. We need more than $2\frac{1}{2}$ million pounds a year to run, so we have to find all our capital and nearly two-thirds of our maintenance and running costs. NHS help is diminishing proportionately as we have responded to needs, extending our work, adding more staff, and getting better and better. Well, that is our fault because we have gone on working and we have refused to let money stop us. But I think they ought to be 50/50, I really do.

We really have been able to make care of dying people into what could now be called a respectable part of medicine; it is seen now as a real medical challenge and not just an amateur, kindly, humanitarian response. I am sorry to illustrate it, but I am an honorary fellow of the Royal College of Surgeons, fellow of the Royal College of Physicians, I got the BMA Gold Medal this year, I have had a number of honorary degrees and so on, which are recognitions that there should be hospice work, there should be special care, there should be special teams in some hospitals, that there should be bereavement counselling. In one sense what we are doing is to work ourselves out of a job, i.e. to say proper care for dying patients should be part of every doctor's and every hospital's remit. It all seems so natural now, but all that has only happened in the last twenty years.

I was once on a panel with four or five other doctors, and they asked us if we would all say how we wanted to die. All the others wanted to die suddenly, like on the golf course, and I was the only one who wanted to die slowly so that I had a chance to say 'Thank you' and 'Sorry' and sort things out and say goodbye properly.

MR JAMES SCOTT
ORTHOPAEDIC SURGEON

═══════

I SPEND some of my time interviewing people who want to become medical students, and often the most interesting ones are those who are not at all sure they want to be doctors; they're more rounded people. One of the great drawbacks about medicine is because it is so institutionalized, you get very tunnel-visioned people doing it. It's a drawback to the profession and it's a drawback to you as a doctor, because it means that all you bring to bear on life is medicine.

Well, for example, one works amazingly stupid hours, to the sacrifice of one's family and to the sacrifice of any sort of hobbies or outside interests that anyone normal would have. When I was a houseman, you were allowed out of hospital every other Saturday night – that was all, the rest of the time you were in hospital. And so from having been an extravagantly carefree, fun-loving medical student, going to parties and the theatre, or popping to Paris for the weekends, and generally having fun, you became an institutional person, and the outside world became a very strange place. And I still find that now.

I say this all the time to my friends: the institutionalization of consultants in the Health Service is the biggest drawback to every aspect of life; I mean, it's a drawback to the future of the profession and it's a drawback to the way in which you approach your patients, particularly in orthopaedics, where we're dealing with the quality of life. For example, all I'm concerned with is making you more comfortable. I operate on your bunion. I take your cartilage out. I give you a new hip. I take discs out of your back – whatever. So when I'm trying to get out of you information so that I can make your life more comfortable, I've got to get a very good idea of what sort of life you lead: is it possible for you to get up and down stairs? can you get to and from the shops? do you take the tube or bus? is sex comfortable? And in order to get the flavour of somebody's life, you have got to have an idea of what all this is like yourself.

To make people feel at ease, I must make them feel that I am a family man, that I go to the shops, that I walk up and down stairs, that I have sex, travel on public transport, that I understand all this business. But, for example, I have not been on a tube for probably nine months or a year. People say to me, 'You know how long it takes to get from Covent Garden to Strand', or wherever, and of course in theory I should do because I have lived all my life in London, but in fact I haven't the first idea. And my point is that the institutional aspect of one's life as a consultant does make quite a lot of these questions a little arbitrary.

Also, it's more difficult for me probing into other people's lives than it is for a general practitioner. I'm in a hospital environment where the patients are outside their normal sphere, and usually I don't know them, I mean, they come from all around the country. If I were a GP somewhere in the country, say a small town or a village, the chances are I would know these people, know their family, know their butcher, know what bus they got on, and just the intimacy of it is very much easier.

You will find the divorce rates of consultants in the Health Service are enormous. I was married before I was qualified. And then I qualified, and it all started, and medicine took over my life, which I loved, but my marriage suffered after six years of junior doctor work, and being in hospital all the time and in different places. I was at the Middlesex for six months, and then at Uxbridge; Swindon for two and half years, Oxford for six months, Hereford for a year, Derby for six months, America for a bit, and I was only coming home every other week. And after a time my wife and I just didn't seem to know each other. We had different lives. I mean, she was the most wonderful person in the world – still is, I see quite a bit of her and we speak lots on the phone. She's married again and lives in Hertfordshire.

The reason the second marriage works is because I come home every night. And that is the bottom line. The awful truth is that's probably the only difference. It is simply if you want a relationship to work you've got to be there and work at it, and being away for thirteen days out of fourteen, you can't have a marriage under those circumstances, and I think it's rather amazing we stayed together as long as we did.

Roughly speaking, our work is divided into two. Those people who have accidents of one sort or another, who come to us through the casualty department, with broken legs, broken any-thing – any sort of fractures or dislocations – we have fracture clinics just for the injured, the halt, the lame and the crippled. They come in an ambulance and are either admitted straight to hospital or they're put in plaster and sent home and told to come to the next clinic, which will hopefully be the next day, and then we see them and do whatever we think best. The other half is what is called cold orthopaedics, which is people going to their G Ps saying, 'I've got a bad leg', 'I've got an arthritic hip', 'I've got a bad back.'

We do a lot of new joints, putting in plastic knees and plastic hips. Putting in a new hip joint is probably the most rewarding operation that we do altogether, because you have frail ladies in pain who cannot walk across the road, and you put a new hip joint in, and it's like buying fifteen years of time.

One day you're just doing spines, the next hips, you can be doing them both on the say day. Well, a spine is much more delicate technically, but otherwise they're not that different.

I do quite a bit of spine work. Spinal surgery mostly involves removing discs, and that is generally for people who've got sciatica or leg pain. I've just seen a man who can't walk across this room with the pain in his legs, been the same for seven months, no doubt at all, he's going to have his disc out in the next two or three weeks. He then will have no pain, he'll be extremely grateful. And that's quite a big operation.

When you remove a disc, the worry, of course, is that you're very, very near the spinal cord. I mean, you're holding the spinal cord in one hand with an instrument while you remove the disc. You remove ligament and bits of soft tissue that are around the spine, and there is the disc, which you then remove with very small little nibblers, curettes, and it comes out looking very much like crab meat, and that's that, then you sew up and go home. It's a much more delicate business than hip work. I mean, with the hip we've got hammers and chisels, whereas inside the spine you've got these very, very fine little instruments.

I do quite a bit of tumour work, and that's very challenging, very enjoyable. Roughly speaking, you're usually making the last weeks or months of people's lives comfortable. If you get cancer of the lung or the breast or cancer of the prostrate, it goes to bone, and then what happens is that your bones break so you can't walk. And our responsibility is to operate on that bone in such a way that you can walk on it. There's no worse way of dying than being bed-ridden where you actually can't get out of bed because your legs are broken.

I actually enjoy all of it. There's a technique called arthroscopy whereby you put a telescope inside the knee and you see cartilages, you see ligaments, linings of joints – it's rather like Jacques Cousteau really, you see all sorts of wonderful things floating around. I mean, roughly speaking, I suppose if we looked at your bowel, and looked at my bowel, inside it would probably look much the same. And I fancy if you looked at the inside of our brains it would probably look much the same. But orthopaedically people look different inside, because joints wear in a different sort of way.

To be a good orthopaedic surgeon you don't have to be very brave, and you don't actually have to be that dextrous, you don't have to be as good with your hands as you do to be a plastic surgeon, but you do need judgement, because you must know when to operate on people. A good operation on the right patient at the right time. It's amazing how many technically wonderful orthopaedic surgeons you will see doing the right operation on the wrong person and making them no better.

You also need phenomenal patience to be a good orthopaedic surgeon. I mean, some of our clinics have got fifty or sixty patients in there, and they're all in pain, and they've all been sitting in our clinic for hours, and they're all cross. And I mean, every surgeon will tell you that occasionally operations will go wrong and there will be blood shooting in every direction and people panicking like mad, particularly people in trauma. Somebody comes in smashed up, with all sorts of broken bits and pieces, and there will be pandemonium going on, and you've just got to produce a lot of calm, and get on with it, calmly and quietly.

The operating room is lovely. The nicest three places are in bed, in the car and in the operating theatre, because the nature of surgery is such that it has to be extremely calm, quiet and well ordered. It's like an extremely posh restaurant. I mean, you can tell when you walk in, can't you, this is a well-organized place: the waiters are all in the right places, the tables are laid nicely, you just feel that it's all going to work properly. A well-run operating theatre is like that. You walk in, you immediately feel at ease, the team, which is all the nurses who are helping you, the anaesthetist, the porters, all the registrars, just have a calmness about them. Wonderful.

Almost everything about my private life is geared to my doctoring life. For instance, I suppose I'm getting old now, but I do find if I have more than a glass or two of wine in an evening I'll wake up with a headache, which I hate if I'm going to operate at 8 o'clock, so I drink very little during the week. I leave the house at quarter past 7, and I'm in the hospital at twenty to 8, and I am then working until 8, 8.30 at night. So I don't see my children at all during the week. And if we go out to dinner or whatever, I make pretty sure that I'm home asleep by midnight. I work most Saturday mornings and I usually pop into the hospital some time on Sunday, and around that life, my private life fits in.

But you ask what would I do if I didn't have my work. It's a wonderful question, that. The answer is that I have every confidence that I would know exactly what to do, and I am also pretty sure that I am wrong. I mean, if you said to me tomorrow, 'Thou shalt not operate', or I raped matron and I was struck off the list, I would like to imagine I would spend my time painting, gardening, travelling, going to matinées and loving it. Actually I think I'd go bonkers in twenty minutes.

When I go on holiday, the first week or ten days are pretty ghastly actually. I'm very restless and I'm ringing up the hospital and fussing away: 'Is Mrs So-and-So all right?' After that I'm usually all right, I get better.

I look at people's deformities, or abnormalities. I mean, you see people who have got arthritic hips or knock knees or club foot or they have obviously had polio, and I just like watching them.

Once in Cheltenham we were in an antique shop, and there was a man who very obviously had got a skin cancer on his face. I didn't buy anything from him, but about a week later it had preyed on my mind so much that I went back to him and I said, 'I'm a surgeon, I don't like the look of what you've got on your face.' In fact he was being treated, so it was all right; he said that he was just going to have it operated on. But it's like the business of rushing up to accidents and saying, 'Don't worry, I'm a doctor' – I really don't like that at all.

One is emotionally involved with most operations really, because by the time you've got as far as operating on those people you know them quite well. I've become very close to a man who had a very, very nasty fracture and almost lost his leg, and it happens we were lucky, and we did what we did, and he's kept it. He's a young man, and he's now running and skiing again and all is well. I got very involved with that man, so that if he felt pain in his leg he would ring me every so often – as a lot of people do – and say, 'James, my leg is hurting me', and that would worry me a lot, because I would worry if the fracture was healing and if we were making the right judgement. On Friday this week I'm operating on a girl of twenty-three who has got a tumour of her rib, from which she will almost certainly die. I mean, the chances of her surviving even a year are only about 10 per cent. And it is going to be an enormous operation. I'm going to take away a great bit of one vertebra and probably four ribs. And I know this girl extremely well now, and I know her family, and we're all locked together. As anybody who does cancer surgery will tell you, it is impossible to do cancer surgery on young people without getting very, very closely, emotionally involved.

It's not possible to do this work without giving the spiritual values an enormous amount of thought almost all the time. But it certainly doesn't make me conventionally Christian. I mean, I go to church now and then, but I think that's more because it's another quite peaceful place.

Orthopaedics has changed phenomenally in the last thirty, forty years. My father was an orthopaedic surgeon, and when he started there were no antibiotics, and anaesthetics was in its infancy. All his early life as a consultant orthopaedic surgeon was spent treating tuberculosis and polio, things I see terribly rarely. Some time during his career they started operating on discs, and towards the end of his life they started putting in new joints. The whole notion, for instance, of looking inside a joint with a telescope would have been extraordinarily alien to him, or even replacing all of the joints that we replace now. I mean, we replace the knee, the elbow, the shoulder, almost everything.

My father and I were always very close, I adored him. But he was very busy, just like me, so I never saw him as a child. The great privilege was to be allowed to sit in his car, to be driven to the hospital on Sundays, and you then were allowed to sit in the car park while he did his ward rounds, and then you were allowed to drive home. And that was almost all I saw of him really, because he got home after I'd gone to bed and he left before I got out of bed in the morning, and we just saw him a bit on holiday. However, he was a most wonderful man. He was terribly calm and gentle, and everything a father should be.

I got to know him very well when he was old. He sort of retired when he was sixty-five, and went into various peripheral bits of orthopaedic administration. I was then becoming a consultant, and by that time he was rather pleased with me – he hadn't been before, he thought I was much too stupid ever to become a surgeon. We were very close for the last two or three years.

I cannot conceive what orthopaedic surgery will be like thirty years from now. The notion is that you're going to be able to grow bone, cartilage, synovium – I mean, everything that makes a joint you'll be able to grow in a laboratory, and then you'll just squirt it in. So they'll look back on this plastic and metal business and think it was absolutely archaic. It's amazing to think about. But we're not going to stop old age and people who are aged are always going to be a prey to all the diseases that go with age, they're all going to fall over and break bones. So orthopaedic surgeons are always going to be needed; it's just the different way in which we treat these old people.

The great issue at the moment, of course, is the organization of the National Health Service, particularly with regard to where the teaching is going to come from. At the moment London is being decimated. What is going to happen to the National Health Service? Hospitals are closing all over the place, and it is increasingly difficult to find beds in which to put your patients, and it's increasingly difficult to employ nurses because there just isn't enough money to pay them. Most of us are despairing of it.

I used to write plays which were put on in the fringe in London, and a couple of weeks at the King's Head at lunchtime, and I loved that. I suppose they were rather juvenile really. But I'd have to call the theatre a hobby. I sort of gibber into a note book for about ten or fifteen minutes most days, first thing in the morning with my first cup of coffee, and some of that gibbering can be dialogue.

I've just written a play which is about doctors, and that play took me about eight years to write, eight years of gibbering. It's mainly about the problems of retirement, which is a golden subject for a play because, I mean, something like a third of hospital consultants will have a coronary within eighteen months of retiring, and that can very easily be dramatized. And what I've done is written about a doctor who, to begin with, you see him retiring and he simply does not know what to do, and they have a ward named after him, and at the end of the play he engineers his admission into his own ward – and he's home. He's blissfully happy in bed, lying out beneath a plaque that says, 'This ward is dedicated to the memory of Dr Jackson.' It's called 'Jackson Ward' because it's Dr Jackson who ends up in his own ward. It's rather moving. I mean, that's what it is like, doctors do retire and go mad or get coronaries.

SISTER MANDY SMITH

NURSE

━━━━━━

I was brought up just outside Southampton. I went to a girls' grammar school which was quite a narrow upbringing in some ways, and then decided to go into nursing when I was thirteen or fourteen. It just seemed to be the thing to do. It's appalling really, I never thought of doing anything else.

At the moment I work on the cancer ward at the Westminster Hospital, so I am looking after patients who are having radiotherapy and chemotherapy, and there is a certain proportion of people who are being cared for terminally, they are not going to go home, they will die on the ward.

It affects me a lot, an awful lot. Often you start questioning the treatments as to how worthwhile they are. You can say to people, 'These are the side effects, and this may not work for you', but nine times out of ten, people will clutch at whatever is available to them irrespective of how awful the treatment is, and opt for spending perhaps the remainder of their life in hospital undergoing quite gruelling treatment.

This happened just last week. A patient was told that there was nothing more that could be done, but there was a treatment that was very much in the early stages that would give unpleasant side effects and may not do any good and would make him feel fairly rotten. Straight away that person said, 'Yes, I'll try it.' My feeling was, 'No, don't try it, go home, enjoy yourself for the last two or three months if you can, see all your friends, whatever . . .' But once that person has made the decision, you obviously go along with it.

Patients are far more deferential to doctors than nurses. Patients' complaints or dissatisfactions about things related to their treatment are very rarely directed to the person that has decided on the treatment, the doctor. Say the side effects of a drug might be making them feel really ghastly, the patient will tell *you* that they feel awful. But on the ward round when the consultant asks if it is bad enough for him to stop the treatment, the patient will say, 'Oh no, it's fine doctor,' and you know damn well that it is not fine, that it is making them feel terrible. There is a lot of that.

This job makes you realize just how fragile life can be. You know the cliché that you can go out and be run over by a bus . . . there is some truth in it. That person in the bed could be you. So it forces you to think about the important aspects of life, and that there is no point moaning over the little things; if the train is ten minutes late, it's not worth getting in a great panic about it, because it is a minor point compared to what can happen.

I'm afraid it does affect your relationships, it can make you quite intolerant. When you are looking after people all day who are extremely poorly, and you get home and the person you live with has got a hangover and is moaning about it, you have got absolutely no tolerance whatsoever, and this is something which an awful lot of nurses feel. It can make your relationship quite fraught. You don't want to hear about people's little niggly problems – to you they are just not worth talking about. But if you don't watch it, you can start thinking that everyone else's jobs are all superficial and that yours is the only one job that matters, which is a load of rubbish.

Nigel has never had any dealing with anybody who is dying, and doesn't really want to; like most young blokes, he doesn't really want to think about death at all. You don't want this girl coming home and saying, 'God, it's awful, there is a patient who has got three children and he is going to die.' Poor Nigel, he tries to understand, but he admits that he doesn't find it easy. He sort of makes an effort to listen, but it's bringing home to him things that he doesn't really want to hear, and he sort of glazes over:

'Oh my God, here we go again.' He came up to my ward, once; that was enough. He didn't have any great desires to come back!

It is absolutely exhausting mentally as well as physically, and it's very hard to switch off, particularly after a late shift, when you get home late at night and have to start work again at 7.30 a.m. the next morning. You have to make quite a big effort to have an outside life. It's very easy to go home and crash out and do very little else apart from the job.

Physically it can be literally non-stop for the entire shift. The physical demands of the job, without the emotion, I think would be OK, but you have got patients who desperately need to talk, you have got their relatives who want your time, and I could easily spend all day just talking to people. If I'm lucky I might have five minutes to get a roll for lunch. If you could get away at lunchtime to an area where you felt relaxed with nice surroundings and decent food, that would play some part in improving things, but when every day you are eating Cornish pasty and baked beans and chips from your canteen, it really is a bit soul-destroying. I think the conditions of service could be greatly improved.

Another thing that gets you: because of the sort of draining side of the job, you tend to feel tired nearly all the time. You can't remember what it is like to wake up in the morning feeling really refreshed. You tend to pick up bugs just because you are working in quite a warm, confined atmosphere, and if one person gets a cold, you can guarantee that five or six other people will as well. I did a nursing research job for a year, which was regular hours, nipping around in a car, and after about a month I felt well for the first time in two or three years, I felt relaxed and healthy and didn't pick up every bug that was passing.

A lot of people can't understand why you do the job, and I think even a lot of nurses don't understand why they carry on. I mean, I don't know what keeps me in the job. I think everyone has times of thumbing through the sits vac in the papers, but something always stops you.

DR NICK THATCHER

ONCOLOGIST

═══════

CANCER'S a lump basically. It's often just white, a white nodule in an internal organ. But the thing is that there are literally hundreds of different types of cancer which all behave in a somewhat different way, and can be widely different in terms of the outcome with surgery, radiation or chemotherapy. So it's wrong to think of cancer as a single disease; there's a whole number of diseases whose character is based upon where the cancer arises.

I deal with two types of cancer mainly: melanomas and lung cancer.

Malignant melanoma usually starts from an ordinary mole or freckle on the skin which can change in size and colour, and you might just like to say in your book that if anyone has a mole which is changing in any way, particularly if it starts bleeding, you should go and see your doctor straight away, because very simple surgery can be lifesaving. If it's left, the melanoma penetrates deeper and spreads to other organs, in which case the outlook is much more serious. So it's very important to get to the doctor early, and that way we might be able to bring down the frightening increase in this disease, which has rocketed up over the last few years. It may be connected with people going abroad, because it's related to sun exposure, so if you get a good tan, it looks nice, but it can also be quite dangerous.

In this country, just with lung cancer, there are over 30,000 deaths a year. Melanoma accounts for a much smaller number, about 2,000. But it's worrying, because it's increasing so fast.

We're interested in melanoma for a number of reasons, including all the humanitarian ones of course, but melanoma is a key cancer because it is so resistant; once it has spread, it's resistant to drugs and all sorts of methods and treatments – and if we could find some way of dealing with it, and treating it, it would have tremendous impact on the whole cancer problem.

There's much more lung cancer in Manchester than elsewhere in the country. It's an enormous difference in fact. A fact of life is that lung cancer patients tend to come from a background of material deprivation, inner-city decay, unemployment, and then there's the women's magazines who promote a svelte body, and it's true that smoking actually helps you lose weight. And the other thing is that cigarette smoking is actually quite a cheap luxury, I mean, it's one of the few luxuries which a lot of unemployed people can afford.

Well, people say life is a fatal disease. What are you trying to do? Prolong life a couple extra years? But that's not the whole object of being a doctor. If an illness isn't amenable to current treatment in terms of survival, you can still help people. What we aim for with someone who's clearly dying, if we can't cure them, at least we can make sure that their last months and days are the best possible.

We don't go around with long faces because it's a cancer ward. It's horrific as far as the personal tragedies of those people, but the attitude is not horrific, it's one of positive approach; you know, the last thing a patient wants is a gloomy-looking doctor or an unhappy-looking nurse.

Well, I can only say how wonderful the patients are. I think I'll leave it at that. I mean, the courage of patients is quite extraordinary. They're given this devastating news, and I can't actually think of one patient that's actually been totally demolished by that. I mean, their attitude and strength is amazing.

I think cancer is still feared, but less so. For example, we can talk much more openly to patients. When I was a young house-man, I have to say that some of the consultants I worked with found it very difficult to talk to a patient who was terminally ill with cancer, and often it would be left to the most junior doctor or nurse to sort of try and stumble through the bad news with the patient. That's now changed, and I think that's a good change.

Well, I tell patients that they've got cancer every day of my working life. I like to think I don't get hard about it, I try to treat every situation individually and be thoughtful about what we say. I think some patients' deaths I've found quite tough, but I don't lose sleep over it – I'm pretty hard in that way.

I had melanoma myself a couple of years ago. I cried when I found out, I have to tell you. Fortunately it was quite a good prognosis and I'm doing all right. But it was very interesting, because I actually left it, I didn't want to distress anyone. It was all the classic mistakes, and I'm an expert in it! There was a thing that started growing on the sole of my foot, and I just refused emotionally to deal with it, and used a whole lot of rationalizations – Christmas time, family, things like that. The thing got bigger and bigger, and round about January or February I went and saw a surgeon, who looked at it. I think to a certain extent no one could believe it was happening, and in fact my friend who's a pathologist made up a spoof report about senile warts and things. I think when he actually found out it was for real, in his own way he was very upset.

Anyway, that was a superficial melanoma, and I think my chances are quite good of it not posing further problems – of survival, basically.

I think what that told me is to try and do as much as you can each day. And that doesn't mean to say I don't have an afternoon's sleep on a sofa, Saturday and Sunday. But I do think time is quite precious, particularly as one gets older. And there are many things I want to do at work – we've got lots of programmes running – and I want to use my time as much as possible to accomplish something each day.

Cancer is very, very difficult to treat because it usually arises from healthy cells, and the only thing that makes a cancer cell different is its capacity to invade, and that makes it very difficult to develop new drugs which will just hit the cancer without damaging the normal cells. But there's a lot of work going on as to why and how it changes to allow it to invade the normal organs and spread, and I think in the foreseeable future, perhaps when I'm still a consultant, we're going to see some really major improvements in cure.

I think doctors in this country are highly regarded, because we're seen to be on the side of the patient. When things start to go wrong, instead of siding with the administration, we take the side of the patient. But people just don't realize what's going on, because most patients are very happy with the NHS, and they trust the doctors and the nurses and the other health workers to maintain it for them.

So it we don't speak up, this terrible situation will continue. You probably don't really understand the contest which is being waged.

What shall I say about the NHS administrators? Well, you could see their types at Nuremberg. To carry out particular orders – on the surface that appears quite reasonable – a health district such as south Manchester has to live within its budget. But the administration says, '. . . We've looked at all the options' – and you never know whether they have or they haven't – 'and the only way to live within a budget is to close wards', which they do.

They don't close empty wards which aren't seeing any patients, they close busy and active wards which see the most patients to make a big impact on cost-cutting. And it's that deliberate policy of turning everything on its head which I find totally unacceptable. And I know they've got mortgages, and I know they've got families, and they're only doing their job, but I just can't cope with that, quite frankly. They're winning the battle, of course. But it doesn't mean that we ought to go down without fighting.

I have to say that's the only thing that I actually lose sleep over: these interminable difficulties with the administration, and trying to prevent their worst excesses.

I think the National Health Service is very efficient, no matter what the detractors say. It's very underfunded compared with the money spent in any civilized country in Western Europe, but it manages, largely through the good will, of the nurses in particular, and the other support services. I mean, everyone thinks of the NHS as the doctors and then the nurses, and they don't think of everything else that goes on: getting the medical records, radiographers, secretaries. And if you've got a great team of these people working, it's crazy not to support it. The country's health is one thing we want to feel secure about, that if we are unwell there is a way of getting the best treatment even if we can't afford it – and that's been eroded. The usual argument is, 'It's a bottomless well' or 'The requirement is infinite. . .': this idea that there will never be enough money for health care is a specious argument, because all we're saying is we should be funded to the same level as our European neighbours, at which level, given the efficiency of the Health Service, we could provide such a vast improvement in health care that it would be astounding.

PROFESSOR PATRICK WALL
NEUROPHYSIOLOGIST

I STARTED at the age of nineteen looking at the brain, and it's immensely exciting now as it was then. It really is the world's last great frontier. I would say personally that beyond seeing a child born, the most dramatic sight that I know is to see a neurosurgical operation where the brain has been exposed. What you see is real drama, that here you are really on the edge of life, and that you or someone else is taking an extreme risk just to look at the thing.

The brain is where you may believe that you, the real Danziger is sitting, and your personality and identity and so on is in there, and the rest is a lot of machinery that is just feeding the real Danziger, and is therefore important but no more important than the telephone line into your house.

But in looking for the real Danny Danziger you are conducting a map-making exercise. You are asking me to point to a place. If I were to come to your motor car, and you tell me that it is a fast car, I might ask you to please point to where the speed of the car is. If speed is a real thing to you, where is velocity in this car? It must have a location. You see, I am suggesting that the mind is a property of the whole thing, and it is not a sensible question to ask me to point at the mind. This business of wanting to label function with a structure that you can point your finger at, that has been classical neurology. Phrenologists said that bumps on your head were measures of brain development and allowed you to point to memory, affection, mathematical ability and so on. Please do not ask me to point to bumps inside your head.

There is a central nervous system, which is the brain and spinal cord, and there is a peripheral nervous system, which consists of nerve fibres which have reached out from the brain and spinal cord into the tissues, either to take orders out or to gather information and bring it in. So you have nerves everywhere in your body, big collections of them, taking orders out, the motor fibres, some bringing information in, collecting all the information. As soon as nerve impulses enter the central nervous system, they are participating in creating this overall dynamic phenomenon which we call mental function.

Physiology really means trying to find out how the body works, and in this case, how the brain helps the body to work. How does the brain receive messages? How does it decide what is going on and generate orders going out to the body?

And my particular area of interest in pursuing these questions is in the spinal cord. You may think that the spinal cord might be a rather curious place to look, but it is a key place because all of the things you know about your body in one way or another are translated into nerve signals which are picked up out in the muscle, or wherever it may be, and transported into the central nervous system. All these messages enter the spinal cord, and immediately upon entry they hit junction points, nerve cells, where lots of calculations go on as to whether they should be further transmitted to the brain, which generates all the reactions. Each of these calculations takes place at decision points, not just simple relays.

That sounds like rather a general thing. But even on a more technical level, the fact is that the spinal cord is not just a simple set of lines going in and out. There is a lot of calculation going on there.

The other thing that I've been particularly looking at is the plasticity of the adult brain, the fact that the adult brain and spinal cord is not what it was classically thought to be, a rather rigidly fixed, hard, wired structure, but it is changing with the environment, and it's changing with disease and so on.

And I can illustrate that best by talking about pain. Classically, and still to a certain extent in the textbooks, pain was thought of as a separate fire alarm system, as though it were screwed on to the structure but completely separate from the rest of the structure. The fire happens, the bell rings – and that's what the pain mechanism was thought to be.

Now, in the past twenty years and more, there's been a real demolition of that attitude, and a substitution of a much more monistic approach in which pain is seen to be something felt in context, and the context is what other things are going on at the moment of an injury and what has gone on in the past, and a prediction of what will happen in the future. The relationship between injury and pain is enormously variable but not random.

I will give you a specific example in terms of pain. Let us talk about an acute sudden injury. When an injury has occurred it generates a message. The messages are delivered to the spinal cord over peripheral nerve fibres, coded messages that are saying such and such an injury has occurred in this place: the spinal cord receives that message and passes it on to cells that will transmit that message to the brain. But the fact is, that message doesn't automatically pass, it depends upon what else is going on, so this is a comparison point, not a relay point. And one of the things that may happen at that point is that the brain says, 'I think the general situation is not relevant to feeling pain at the moment, so do not transmit that message.' Now, that decision is being taken right at the very first entry point into the spinal cord, and we call that a 'Gate Control', it is a control of the entry of information.

But I will tell you a very funny thing. If you talk about the function of pain, there are certainly people, the present Pope for example, who would speak of noble suffering and of suffering which reminds you of your mortality and your salvation and so on. He is assigning a function to pain, he is being a neuro-physiologist in a way.

I investigate single nerve cells or single nerve fibres or even a single system which may produce pain. They certainly exist, but not as a fire alarm system. The brain is wonderfully subtle. It is an integrated whole, not a collection of separate bits.

The brain reacts to much less dramatic events. If you tell me that you know there was a storm last Friday, you have changed your brain in the process of remembering. You've inserted that phenomenon in your brain; part of your brain has been changed by the storm last Friday.

Perhaps you fancied a girl momentarily on the train. An hour later you may have remembered the incident, although a week later or a month later you might not. But that would certainly have given you a tweak, changed your heart rate, your endocrine system will have changed. And those changes are never momentary, they always have a long-lasting tail to them. If you admit that memory is a property of the brain, then obviously the brain has to be changing with the environment. In one sense that's an absolute platitude – you learn by changing your brain.

It's the other sort of mind-bending, with drugs, that I think we're exceedingly bad at, and the use of tranquillizers is completely out of control. I'm telling you that drugs such as tranquillizers are acts of brain surgery. You are putting a chemical weapon through the system, not a knife, admittedly, but another form of warfare. And the tranquillizer works by going into the brain and paralysing certain bits of the brain, and having done so, it is to a certain extent irreversible. The brain is not just a passive machine. It reacts to drugs or to surgery or to disease by changing, and sometimes it changes irreversibly.

But exactly what constitutes that change, that's one of *the* major questions now of neurobiology.

All of us who are involved in this particular type of science are code-cracking. You are plugged into a system which is clearly communicating from one place to another and making decisions, and you do not know what the code is, although you may have observations of the input and the output. I'll give an analogy. You may be observing two military establishments that are sending messages from one to the other, and they've got a very clever coding system and you're unable to break the code. So you watch to see something that happens regularly, such as the men changing guard, and spot a message that is associated with the guard change. And that's the way to get into code-cracking; in other words, to stand back and see some disturbance in the system that's associated with some particular message. You know that the Enigma Code, which was changed every day, they had an enormous race every morning to see if they could crack the code, and they had all sorts of tricks if they could not crack that day's cipher. For example, they would send a plane up to a harbour simply to sink a buoy, because they knew that the German coast guard would report that buoy number 16B had been sunk and ought to be replaced. They had forced the system to send a coded message, and that eventually allowed them to crack the entire code. Now, that's what good neurophysiology does, to stand back and try to correlate some meaningful action of the body involving the brain and to try to discover the types of messages that are associated with it.

So, I spend my time code-cracking. We're getting there, I would say, and in getting there one finds that there is not a single message that means pain. And on thinking back over the problem that's probably expectable. I'll give you a specific example we're working on right at the moment. If you look in any peripheral nerve, you find a group of very small nerve fibres called C-fibres, and the discovery is that these C-fibres are literally tasting the tissue that they are in, and their chemistry is fundamentally changed if you switch them to grow in different areas. In other words they are recognizing their target in terms of chemistry. We simply don't know what they're doing. They're something to do with disease, but it is not clear what their function is. Strong suspicion that they're something to do with pain and disease, but that's a good problem to be working on.

This really is an absolutely fascinating highway where one might be able to influence the pains of people who have nerve damage. That is a conceivable target. But let us suppose one managed it. It would be merely a step along a huge road trying to explain what the nervous system does, and how it's doing it, although along that road one could identify some nearby cross-roads where you might hope to be able to influence whether you turn left or right: we haven't solved the problems of geography only a particular issue of route.

People don't know much about their bodies. The general knowledge of the body, even in the vaguest sense, is very low. It's horrific and it simply astonishes me. The standard of reporting in the newspapers – any newspapers! If you look at a discussion of, let us say, nuclear power, a very high percentage of the population knows the difference between plutonium and uranium, and fission and fusion, and these words are plonked in the quality papers without apology.

Presumably the reason why people know about atom bombs is that somebody in the City feels he ought to know about it, whereas your liver – good heavens! That sounds like something for butchers, 'not a gentlemen's concern'. I mean, we're still in that era. What your kidneys are doing, let alone the brain – it's all getting down to unspeakable matters which are really of no interest to proper-thinking people.

I regard the kidney, the liver and the brain as the great intellectual challenges that remain. I really mean an intellectual, philosophical, aesthetic challenge. Here is a world of interesting exploration and puzzlement and ignorance and so on, and there are precious few such things that you could point to. You point to a painting, let us say. Everybody knows the names of the great classics and a few modern painters. The artist is exploring the relationship between his senses and the outside world, if he's a realist artist. And that is exactly what you are doing in neurophysiology, with different tools, different philosophical approach, but it is precisely that. I'm saying that the brain has at least equal fields of equal fascination to explore.

You ask how my work affects me as a person. I think to begin with that you've got to be a particular sort of person in the first place, with a lot of very unpleasant characteristics: to be obsessional, to be rather introspective, to be able to be lonely, to be able to put up with the loneliness of the long-distance runner – in the sense that if you're at the frontier, you're really there, you are by yourself, there's nobody else with you. There are people behind you and people in other parts of the frontier, but *you're it*, and that's a pretty frightening and depressing place to be.

It can make you a fairly mean, miserable, unapproachable character, and I think it's contributed to that, although it may have been my character in the first place.

I would say it has caused some problems, yes. Oh yes. Some of them I positively like. I like being contentious. I like being different; I'm not desperately anxious to be the same as everybody else and to join in their Gilbert and Sullivan, 'You're right and I'm right and all is right' situation, which some people simply adore.

But I have been married and I would say that undoubtedly some of those problems were related – I don't think caused – by being a scientist, and probably some of the same characteristics of independence, of standing off by myself, almost appreciating my loneliness, probably contributed to the failure of that marriage.

DR RICHARD WARNER

HOUSEMAN

═══════

YOU'VE come at a bad time. Well, you see, we admitted some-body yesterday, somebody who was poorly, and we didn't know what was wrong so we left her on the ward to see if things got better; but it became obvious she'd got an appendicitis which had perforated, so the bowel contents were leaking into the belly. Once we decided what to do, we went straight ahead and booked the theatre, booked the anaesthetist, and half past two I rang the ward to see whether the patient had been seen by the anaesthetist, and she hadn't, so I had to find out why. And we've had a huge bunch of people in casualty, two of whom had stopped breathing. One was a road accident. I went down there to try and find my anaesthetist and it was like bedlam, people throwing things through the doors and running around the department, just awful, so I decided eventually that the best thing to do was to bleep the second on-call anaesthetist. He was delivering a baby, and, can you believe it, the third on-call anaesthetist was also delivering another baby, so we were stuck, we didn't have an anaesthetist. So I had to sort one out, and eventually I met my registrar in the corridor, he's like the guy next up from me, and we went down to casualty and we actually went into the scrum and winkled out the first anaesthetist and said, 'Come on, you must operate on our girl because she's going off quickly', and he said, 'Yeah, sure', and as we were going out we rang the theatre, who told us they had put another case where we were supposed to be because it was so busy! It's just like juggling, and it basically means you spend ages on the phone; we call doctors in casualty with a special code on the phone, but every time I used the code it was engaged, so I was literally taking about ten minutes to make a call.

And then there were things going on in the ward, because I cover the wards during the day, and at the moment I happen to have got about three or four ill patients and have to do everyday things for them like blood tests and forms and things like this, and it just means you get bombarded from all directions, and you've only got one brain and one pair of hands, and when everyone throws things on you in a big heap, you just have to try and put things in order of priority. And when the thing you are trying to put first in order of priority is impossible to organize, like getting the girl to theatre, it's a nightmare.

She's on the wards now. I mean, she's quite well, she's got everything she needs at the moment, she's got pain relief and fluids going into her veins and she's got somebody looking closely at her in case she becomes iller, but what we really need to do is stop the bowel contents leaking into the peritoneum – which you can only do by sewing up the hole. She's only going to get worse, she won't get better if she's got a hole in her bowel.

I don't think she will pop off. I mean, it would take her a couple of days to go, but the point is it's the weekend coming up and over the weekend there's just on-call people: there's two house surgeons and a registrar and a few medics as well, but that's it. I mean, the whole of the hospital winds down over the weekend and if anything bad happens your facilities and your ability to cope are considerably reduced. So you want to get things sorted out before the weekend, and that's why today there's such a rush on. I was going to go out this evening but it doesn't look like I'm going to now . . .

I get hassled, everyone gets hassled occasionally, but all it is really is the limit at which you can pretend you're not hassled, if you see what I mean. I'm not hassled at the moment even though there is quite a lot going on, but if you put a little bit more on to me, heap me with a little more work, I would be hassled, yes.

There are some things I would rather didn't happen to me

until I'm experienced enough to cope with it. I really hated it when one of the guys on the wards had this big belly wound that went from the umbilicus to the suprapubis region, and had a great hole there with what looked like just a little bit of infection, and the registrar stuck his probe up and into it, and it went into a big cavity at the top and a big cavity at the bottom, and he took a knife and it fell apart – and all this stuff came out, green muck, pus, and pieces of nylon, which is the stuff they use to sew it with. I'd had too much to drink the night before, and I just sort of had to go out of the curtain and have a breath of fresh air, because of the smell basically, but I mean even the sister who had been there for twenty-five years found it a bit much.

I've been in the job three months. As it turns out, all I do is very minimal sort of easy things, which isn't what the general public think of as a doctor. I clerk people when they come in, do routine tests, and occasionally do very simple techniques to help people, nothing which you would consider to be particularly glorious or clever, nothing sort of prestigious, but I enjoy it anyway because they're just little things that make people more comfortable.

I'm a houseman. It's a beginning; I'm twenty-three and it's the first step on the ladder. In the medical field you can drift, or you can go hell for leather for a certain career. Some people have just got it in their heads right from the start they are going to be brain surgeons and they attack that idea, they're very aggressive about it, they have to get the right job for the next stage in their career ladder. I'm going to be one of the people that just drifts, and I might even end outside medicine; I'm not really sure yet. My heart's not in the sacrifices you have to make in order to go for the one particular career.

I had a choice between music or medicine, and I'd have preferred to do music in some ways because it's aesthetically more pleasing, but it wasn't secure enough, especially in Coventry, where I'm from. I just wanted to do something where I went to work every day, and I happened to be good at the sciences, and also I quite liked the glamorous idea of being a doctor. I'm not like some people for whom medicine is all-consuming; you know, it's just a job really. I felt I had a choice, and because I actually enjoy doing it, it means that it was the right thing to do, but if at some point I decide I'm not enjoying it, I'll go off and do something else. And if I don't become a consultant, it's not going to be the end of the world.

I really don't believe that I'm a doctor. It's all come as a big surprise. I was a student, and now, suddenly, I'm a doctor. I still feel totally young and stupid; I don't feel the least bit grown-up yet, because every single time somebody talks to you, either a nurse or a physio or a pharmacist or a senior member of the medical staff, every single comment is tailored to someone who is still a school boy. I really do feel like a new boy at school. An experienced nurse, for instance, knows a lot more than a newly qualified doctor does on a ward. The best people to work with are the people who are able to tell you what you are doing wrong without destroying your confidence.

It takes a lot out of you. You give too much and you end up being drained emotionally and physically. Giving all the time can destroy you and people become embittered by the fact that they have to always be reasonable and rational when things happen which aren't reasonable and rational.

Things like somebody who has a small little lump in their bowel, and you say, 'Oh, well, we should be able to cure you', and then the house report is something horrendous . . . a horrendonoma! You can't really say, 'That's tough, I'm sorry', and walk away; you have to talk to them and be nice to them. It's the same situation as if you have just finished with your girlfriend and she wants to keep seeing you and you have to keep going along and saying hello and being nice, but really it's just making you feel sick inside.

Youngsters come in, kiddies, and die in casualty, and I haven't actually had to do it yet, but I can't imagine going out there and saying, 'Listen, sorry, but your five-year-old is dead . . .' What then? You really haven't anything to offer. All you can say is, we did our best.

I always used to think you have to come up with something brilliant to put everyone at their ease, and not get too embarrassed when people are going to die and you get all the sort of high-tension emotional scenarios. They are actually not as critical as I thought they were. I've always thought, maybe I couldn't produce the goods, but really I don't have to produce any goods, I just have to sit there and even if I don't say anything concrete, as long as they feel that somebody has actually bothered and is doing something about it, it's enough.

I've only had to tell one person so far that they were going to go; it's 'Good Night, Vienna.' It upset me a lot.

I'm less upset about death now. Some people should die. I mean, I'm not going to make them die, but they are sitting there, they're blind, diabetic, demented, they've got pneumonia, they have a colostomy bag, they've got nothing going for them, they don't understand what's happening to them, they just plead all night and all day to die, and they get a chest infection and you give them a course of antibiotics, and in some ways you feel you're being immoral doing that, but it's not really there for you to judge, it's just for you to help. But when they die I'm positively glad sometimes and it's only humane to feel that really.

It's made me more appreciative of health and happiness; you know, seeing so much going on around you really makes you enjoy being happy and well. And it's also given me a strong feeling of fate; you know, sometimes somebody has got it in for a certain patient and no matter how good you are, no matter what you do, things keep going wrong, and you just get this feeling that it's a bit beyond your control really.

Well, I like to think I work very hard. The job comes in fits and starts; some weeks you can be really quiet and you've got a bit of time to sit and think and have a lunch hour, and some weeks you can be up with the lark and go to bed half past 1, 2 in the morning, be up two or three times in the night, and start work again at 7. That can go on for a good week's stretch, and it's after that that you really need your time off.

I make valiant efforts to meet people outside medicine because you do find you become totally blinkered and introverted. I have got nurse girlfriends, but it's because they're forced on you, because they are the people who are around. I'd like to marry an opera singer or something, that would be fun, it would be an escape when you got home from the hospital.

I can only go out every other weekend and every two nights in three during the week, so of course it cuts into my social life. But the thing is, I have a philosophy of making the nights off harder work than the nights on because otherwise if you let it stop you doing things, like having a beer in the evenings, if it stopped you doing that then it's interfering too much. Some people go to bed at 9 o'clock because they're tired. But even if I'm tired I get on the tube and go into London and come back even more tired, but at least I've done something, I've gone out, I haven't just sat in the hospital, because that can be a really negative, destructive process.

I feel like I've aged about ten years in the past three months. I feel like I've got grey hair, lines. I feel all the sort of carefree student existence has just evaporated. One minute you don't have to get up in the morning and you don't have to take your work too seriously, next minute you're being screamed out of theatre for doing something. The whole world changes as soon as you qualify, and they expect you to just cope.

I was not prepared for the onslaught. I had my expectations of what the job was when I was a clinical student, I thought I knew what was going to happen, but I didn't quite realize the ferocity of such responsibility. I mean, everything really comes on to your shoulders in a big way, like instead of making decisions in a theoretical context in front of the consultant, '. . . Well, we could perform a laparotomy . . .' Suddenly it's you that's doing it, and it makes things totally different, it sharpens up your wits and your instincts no end. Immediately you become a lot more astute, not because you become cleverer but because you have to put what few bits of knowledge you've got into some sort of sem-blance of a rational decision. I hated it at first because it was so foreign to me, but now I quite enjoy it; especially when you get it right, it gives you a nice feeling afterwards.

PROFESSOR SIR DAVID
WEATHERALL
MOLECULAR BIOLOGIST

I suppose the word 'gene' was derived from Mendel's work, in which he showed certain genetic characteristics were handed down from generation to generation, and he called the things that determined these characteristics genes. People knew about DNA long before Watson and Crick, but they didn't know that it was *the* genetic material until the famous paper they published in *Nature* in 1953. And that was probably one of the most important biological discoveries ever. In fact every cell in the body has DNA, and in that DNA is the genetic information for the entire human being. And what they described was a chemical which could essentially reproduce itself extremely accurately – and that's what a gene is, a gene is a little section of DNA which has the chemical information for one particular characteristic. What it actually does is to tell you how to make a protein: protein's the kind of building-block of all of us really, and proteins vary tremendously from tissue to tissue because of the order of their building-blocks, which are called amino acids. The whole variability of all living species depends on the order of these amino acids that make up proteins, and so the gene directs the order of amino acids for a particular protein, and therefore makes sure that that protein is the right shape and size and consistency for a particular tissue.

There's an enormous amount of DNA in the body. To give you an idea, a cell is something you can just about see under a microscope that will magnify things a few hundred times – and if

I were to take one of those cells and extract the DNA, there's actually two metres of very tightly coiled DNA in every cell. And some clown has calculated that if you've got two metres in every cell, and there's about three times ten to the twelfth cells in the body, that's six times ten to the twelfth metres of DNA; if you unravelled it all and joined it end to end, it would stretch to the moon and back 8,000 times! So there's an awful lot of DNA, and we don't know what an awful lot of it does. There may be something like – well, a guess – a few hundred thousand genes that direct the structure of different proteins, but that only accounts for a very small part of the total DNA.

One of the great things about DNA is that it's not perfect. If a chemist had made DNA, he would have made an absolutely perfect replicating molecule. But DNA makes mistakes, and because DNA makes mistakes, we can therefore have natural selection; in other words, we can start to breed new species, and therefore it is possible to go right back to imagine that the first life on the planet was a pure chance event, that you had a kind of primeval soup with molecules floating around, and there was a flash of lightning and something came together, and by chance you made a replicating molecule like DNA, which has had the ability over millions of years to make mistakes, some good, some bad. Now, if it's a bad change, or mutation, then it will cause disease and it will get wiped out. But if it were a perfect molecule that replicated exactly the same every time, we'd probably still be living in the primeval soup.

I mean, is there any grand scheme? The answer could very well be no. The original chances that produced a replicating molecule that was capable of making the odd mistake was all we needed, the rest just followed – by chance. It's like an enormous lottery with the chromosomes being the lottery numbers. There are very respectable scientists, for example people like Fred Hoyle, who would say this is about as likely as a whirlwind blowing through a junkyard and putting together a Boeing 747. And Francis Crick has come to the view that maybe the first replicating molecules came from outer space.

Well, I don't personally have any kind of religious affiliation, but none of that explains things like first causes. I mean, I think it makes somebody operating all this rather unnecessary, because if one assumes that it's a great lottery, and I have found virtually nothing that's incompatible with that view, then there doesn't seem to need to be any kind of grand master-plan behind it.

I think the next major step in human genetics will be the ability to correct genetic diseases to some degree. We're talking about simple gene transfer between tissues, to transfer normal genes into people with bad genes, probably in the next five or ten years. This is no different in principle than what they're doing already with organ transplants – at the moment we transplant healthy organs like kidneys and hearts, and in the future, if you've got a single gene that's wonky and makes you sick, the idea will be to transplant that with a healthy one.

I hope we're not ever talking about putting genes in embryo into future generations because that would be meddling with evolution, and I think it would be very unwise to embark on that kind of course.

The amount of genetic information to make a human being is enormous, and at the moment we're tackling it kind of one gene at a time. The scientific community has probably isolated 2 or 300 human genes – and we may in the end be having to look for 50 to 100,000, something like that. And the total genome and the total DNA which govern the body are extremely large, and so there are plans at the moment to produce a map of the entire human genome, like a dictionary, so that you end up with what's called a gene library that represents almost the entire complement of anybody's DNA; whether blue eyes or any genetic trait, you'll just look up and say, 'I want to study the gene for haemoglobin from a sick child', and so I can go into my library and fish out the gene for haemoglobin, or haemophilia or whatever. The ultimate aim, I suppose, in this field would be to be able to explain human beings down to the last kind of building-block of their DNA.

By and large we reduce the simple genetic traits that we work with into very straightforward biochemical terms. Whether it will ever be possible to explain human behaviour – you know, the ability to write the Choral Symphony or something like that in terms of the chemical make-up of a length of D N A – I'm not so sure. I think the human behavioural patterns are probably very complex interactions of your genetic make-up and your environment. It may be that an extreme talent will turn out to be explainable on genetic grounds, but at the moment we're dealing with extremely simple genetic traits that you can trace through families.

There's a certain frustration, and a scientific danger really, in wanting to know too many answers because so much is now possible.

What we want to find out – in a sense that's a non-question to somebody who's interested in science of any kind, because there's no final answer. Whenever you find an answer to a problem, it really just forms the basis for the next one. It's a continuous process, I don't have a kind of final end point.

Well, obviously we've been dealing with the very simplest of genetic problems. What I would like to find out ultimately is the genetic component of much more complex diseases, like heart disease, psychiatric disease, cancer and so on, which I think is where this field is going to lead in the future. If I understood the true cause of those diseases, I'd be able to treat them much more logically, I think. I wouldn't be involved in all this high-technology patch-up type procedures like transplants, coronary artery surgery.

Well, we don't know for sure yet, but it's looking more and more as though cancer is the end point of a whole series of different genetic chance events. It may be made more likely that that chance event will be more likely if you expose yourself to tobacco smoke or different environmental factors, but ultimately, it's all a big game of dice.

If you're going to do decent research, you've got to be very focused on the problem in hand. You tend to think just within the limits of what are feasible scientific questions. You don't expect science to answer the ultimate questions about why we're here and all that kind of thing, because they're probably not questions that can be asked within the framework of scientific method as we know it.

You're doing this sophisticated science, and then you come into the wards and have to make the transition from precision to total imprecision. And you go down to outpatients, and you see a patient with something that is totally non-definable by modern medical science. You've then got to realize that despite all the science, a big hunk of modern medicine is still very much an art form ... I mean, it is talking to people, it's making a fairly imprecise guess at what's the matter with them, and it's taking available treatment, which is often kind of arbitrary treatment, and you're moving from very clean science to extremely dirty science. I mean, if you're sick, you don't want a scientist talking to you with precise descriptions of your molecules; you want somebody who can give you a bit of comfort and talk in very simple terms about what he's going to do about it. The decent doctor shouldn't be deluding himself, but he may have to delude his patients to some degree because he knows that a lot of the advice he's giving and the things he's doing are imprecise and uncertain on a scientific basis.

Going from scientist to doctor is the hardest thing in the world actually. And if you're not careful, if you try and take the science into the wards too much, you become a kind of total nihilist. You do nothing because you know that the vast majority of medical treatment is still very much a kind of ... well, it's a kind of educated guess.

I think it's essential that some people do try and keep a foot in both worlds, because somebody's got to be able to talk to the basic scientist and to the clinician, and if people don't try and keep in both camps, the two worlds will get separated and will not communicate, and all the benefit will be lost.

The worst part of my life is stupid administration really. I mean, the hours you spend on things like NHS committees, trying to sort out ways of keeping the Health Service running with gradually diminishing funding and awful bed crises and trying to sort out how you're going to keep the place going with the cuts, and endless hours spent writing grant applications, trying to bring money into the place for research.

It's pretty gloomy here, like everywhere: enormous cuts, beds shut, inadequate clinical facilities, inadequate facilities for the students. We've been very lucky on the research side because we've been able to raise a big pile of money for this new institute for molecular medicine, but the Health Service side has been particularly difficult.

I think that the Health Service is a marvellous institution, and I think we've got to keep it. The big difficulty is that the country is expecting a standard of health care way and above what it's paying for. We're paying about 6 per cent of our GNP on health compared with, say, 15 per cent in a lot of Europe, and I don't think the government's got to grips with this at all. The people on the street expect a first-class health service, and they're not paying for it – the politicians have not told the public what it costs to run the kind of Health Service which they expect. I don't think *they* know. The thing I find most depressing is that I don't find people in Health Service politics with any clear feel for the future, how we are going to cope with the increasing elderly population and so on.

At the moment there's a misconception by government of what health care and doctoring really is about. I think the present government looks upon it as a kind of industry which has got to be more and more efficient, and I don't think that they have grasped that running a hospital must be, by definition, an inefficient process. If I've got a finite number of beds, and tonight I'm going to have five emergencies, and tomorrow night I'm going to have forty-five emergencies, it's impossible for me to tell from day one how they're going to do, whether some of them are going to be uncomplicated or complicated. So to organize that on a kind of Sainsbury's basis is just not possible. I mean, in trying to meet the government demands for efficiency, what's happening is that we're making our hospitals into a kind of rapidly turning over first-aid post, and the standards of clinical care and particularly pastoral care – I mean the time to sit and talk to people and look after them as one would like to – are being eroded all the time. There are inefficiencies, I'm sure, but we've cut back, cut back and cut back to ridiculous lengths.

I think you've got to sit back and say, 'How many beds do we need? How are we to look after our elderly population in the community? What kind of facilities do they need?' and, 'How much is it going to cost?' It should be fairly simple. It'll cost a lot more than is being put in.

But there's no ideal set-up in the world. I had a conversation with a young chief resident in Los Angeles last week: I asked, 'Are you enjoying this job?' and he said, 'No. It's miserable. We haven't got enough beds and I spend my days wandering around this extremely expensive hospital with original Picassos on the wall, trying to find beds.' I think health care has just caught every population totally by surprise because of the post-war successes with combating infection, people living longer and longer. But at the same time, we've not got on top of the basic diseases of Western society like heart disease and strokes and so on, and we probably won't for quite a long time, and therefore the whole thing is exactly opposite to what Bevan thought might happen, that it would get less and less expensive as society got more and more healthy. But of course it doesn't. Just the opposite. And nobody's got to grips with this.

We're lagging behind in the scientific field in this country; it's quite serious. But the reasons for lagging behind are very complicated really, partly based on the way doctors are trained more in the art of medicine than in the science of medicine; there's a curious kind of dichotomy between science and medicine in this country, and in the medical profession itself there's almost an anti-science kind of ethos which you don't come across in North America. I mean, the sciences in this country are looked upon a bit like a kind of perfectly respectable pastime for clever people, but not really practically important.

I don't expect the public to know all about molecular biology, but I think that it's the duty of people like myself to educate them a little, because ultimately this new ability to understand the human genome is going to raise all sorts of moral and ethical questions, and I don't see how you can have a kind of informed public debate on some of these without increased knowledge. I read the Hansard Report of the debate they had in parliament last year on embryo research, and that was awful really because it was so low level, I mean, the scientific input was at such a level of ignorance that it was frightening.

And of course there *are* specific moral and ethical questions. How far should we go along the lines of screening populations for genetic disease? Advising women who are carrying babies with genetic defects to have pregnancies terminated? How far should we be allowed to go along the lines of so-called gene therapy in altering people's genetic make-up? These are very difficult questions, and I think unless you've got a population that can at least understand the principles of their genes and what the doctors might be wanting to do to them, you can't start a debate. It's a failing in the education system; it goes right back to the kind of ridiculous way in which people are educated in this country whereby they specialize almost before puberty. I was just talking to some of my son's friends from Cambridge at the weekend. The kids were doing Arts subjects, and these very bright kids told me that they'd done no science since they were fourteen.

And then our media — I have to say! I was staggered last week to read the science coverage in something like the *New York Times* compared with our daily newspapers here. The *New York Times* last week had a whole page on some aspect of genetic engineering, and it was a superb piece of journalism actually, and how often would you see a full spread in our papers? Well, you don't.

When I'm walking down a street in a big city in the States or in South-East Asia somewhere, I look at people with a certain amount of wonderment at the extraordinary kind of diversity of *Homo sapiens*. In Los Angeles last week, looking at this extraordinary kind of racial hodgepodge, it is quite extraordinary really how the human race has got kind of mixed and diversified.

Funnily enough, I don't do it walking down a street in Oxford, where I live. You're usually kind of keeping an eye on the extremely bizarre characters that populate the streets in the winter, and in the summer you're just trying to avoid the Japanese.

PROFESSOR ROBERT WINSTON

GYNAECOLOGIST, SPECIALIST IN IVF
(IN VITRO FERTILIZATION)

W ELL, I had been interested in the fallopian tube, which is the part of the body which conducts the egg down from the ovary into the uterus, and I'd been appalled by the crudity of the surgery that was done on it; the internal diameter down which the egg passes is only half a millimetre, and conventional surgery to repair that was being done using the naked eye, and it struck me that the new methods of microsurgery which were being used in plastic surgery might be applicable to this kind of surgery. So basically, I took the microscope into tubal surgery, and developed the field of tubal microsurgery. I also tried, perhaps very imperfectly, to look at a number of physiological aspects of tubal transports. I was interested in how eggs and sperm were transported into or away from the uterus, and the microsurgical tools enabled one to study a number of aspects which were not just related to treatment of tubal blockage but also to tubal function. Our work has been developed all around the world by numerous other workers since, I mean, tubal microsurgery is now the standard method for dealing with a whole range of reproductive research experiments.

And my practice in tubal surgery has become by far the biggest and the most successful in the world, which has been both a blessing and a curse. It's been a huge advantage, because it has brought financial security to the unit, which has meant that I have been able to earn fees from overseas patients which have gone into a charitable trust which has funded my unit, and without which I couldn't have done the things that I have done.

The curse is that everybody wants me to operate on them, and I probably see more patients in a clinic than any other consultant in the whole of Hammersmith Hospital. I would doubt if there were many gynaecologists who see as many new patients each week as I do. The average gynaecologist would see maybe six or ten new patients each week; I will see three or four times that number quite regularly, and that is a huge burden, especially as my patients are patients with emotional and psychosexual problems, patients who need a great deal of discussion unravelling their problems, not just surgical treatment.

Well, 95 per cent of the patients that I see have already seen other consultants complaining of infertility, and that treatment has failed, so we are seeing the hard core. And in the main they are coming either for surgical treatment of their tubal disease or for *in vitro* fertilization, the test tube baby treatment. Our *in vitro* fertilization programme has been built up steadily and it is now not only the biggest on an NHS academic site in this country, but it is certainly the most successful. I mean, the latest report showed that per treatment cycle, 8·5 per cent of patients had a live baby throughout the United Kingdom – although I know the press make it sound more successful than that – and of course, the Hammersmith figures are added into those, but to give you an idea of how different we are from the national average, 47 per cent of our embryo transfers have resulted in a pregnancy, so it is a phenomenally successful programme and very well designed.

Now, the sort of patient that I see might typically be a woman who is perhaps thirty-five, who has been trying for a baby for twelve years, who has seen at least three other consultant gynaecologists during that time, who has probably had some unsuccessful surgery, who may have quite severe emotional problems, whose sexual life is to say the least very inadequate. Her husband may quite often be impotent or have problems as a result of the stress that the impotency has caused. That is quite a common kind of scenario. And they have to decide whether they accept the fertility problem as it is, or whether they go through further investigation, and if they go through further investigation, whether they go for highly unsuccessful test tube baby treatment, or whether they look for other options.

The test tube baby publicity has been a disaster for infertile people, because it has given them the impression that the treatment is much more successful than it really is. And I think some of my famous colleagues have been very reprehensible in their attitude. People like Patrick Steptoe in some ways have done a great disservice because they sought publicity for this treatment and gave the impression that it is more successful that it really is. And that has led people to believe that the baby is just around the corner, with headlines like 'New Hope for Childless Women' occurring in newspapers all the time.

These people are going through murder. You have women who are going through annual major operations in an effort to get children. Test tube baby treatment is incredibly emotionally demanding, extremely destructive, and requires vigorous and appalling commitment.

Any test tube baby programme depends upon a series of fences, like the Grand National. Just having got on to the programme is the first hurdle. Most test tube baby programmes, except the very private ones, have a two- to four-year waiting list to get on them, and all those patients will have had endless investigations. They will have come across doctors who are really not interested in infertility, because it doesn't kill you, who don't have any kind of sensitivity about what is involved with infertility, who do one test at a time and never completely give them the full information. Most of these women will have been to clinics where they are told one thing one month, and three months later, they are told an entirely different diagnosis. Finally, they persuade the general practitioner to refer them to a test tube baby programme, where they wait on a waiting list.

And then comes the great day, which requires them giving up an entire month – they mustn't work during that month. On our programme they have to be at the hospital every day for scanning first thing in the morning, they have to have daily blood samples, and at any stage of that, day by day as their hormone levels change, we may decide that the whole treatment needs to be cancelled because the eggs aren't developing properly. They may successfully get to the egg collection stage, which is a surgical procedure to remove eggs from the ovary, and that too may be abandoned at the last minute, so that is another hurdle. Alternatively, they may go for egg collection, be anaesthetized, and the surgeon doesn't collect any eggs. Having got to egg collection, and got eggs, the husband then has to produce semen, and by this time he is usually so screwed up that producing semen, which has to be produced in the hospital in sterile circumstances in a special bedroom, may be very difficult. Sometimes they can't masturbate, there is no way that they can ejaculate as the stress is so severe. Or they produce semen which is subfertile – so that is another problem. And then, of course, you get the semen but the eggs don't fertilize, or if they fertilize, two days later the embryos don't develop. And most commonly, you put the eggs back into the uterus, and two weeks later the woman has a menstrual period, when of course she believed that she was pregnant. Or worse still, she actually has an early pregnancy, but as happens with a very large number of these women, they miscarry. So it is a highly demanding treatment.

It is very difficult for someone who is not infertile and who has never faced this problem to realize how big a problem it is. It is huge. When you are infertile – and one in eight couples in this country are infertile, so it is bloody common – it doesn't affect you for the first year or two at all: '. . . We can do without children, they're a nuisance . . .' As you get older, there is a major sense of fulfilment lacking, and then there is a loss of self-esteem, and you believe that you have let your partner down. So there is a feeling of recrimination between the two of you, and this can eat away. Then in your early thirties, which is when most people start going to things like dinner parties, everyone around the table has got children at school, it is the usual topic of conversation – except for the infertile couple. Infertile couples commonly withdraw, and tend not to go into rooms where there are young children or pregnant women about, or where people are going to be discussing any aspect of their family over the dinner table. And there is the embarrassment that the other people feel on their behalf. In the meantime their parents are saying, 'Why hasn't John got children . . . it must be Mary's fault. I knew he shouldn't have married her . . .' So, with this pressure as well in the background, it compounds things, and over the years it becomes a major, major issue.

And the corrosive aspect of that is severe, and to give you an idea of how severe it is, women who are infertile with tubal disease may go through five or six abdominal operations in an attempt to have a child, the sorts of things that you or I wouldn't dream of doing because we would find it too painful and too physically invasive. And they will do it without a trace of hesitation. My record is fifteen. Fifteen operative procedures on one patient, Mrs Wilmington, and she didn't get pregnant.

There are literally dozens of reasons for being infertile. 30 per cent of infertility is due to the man primarily, there is something wrong with the sperm. We are a comprehensive reproductive unit, so we can deal with it, but unfortunately male treatments are not very successful. Tubal damage and tubal disease are a major component. Failure to produce eggs is a third major component. But there are many other causes of infertility, which include an abnormal uterus, or some other problem in the body's environment, damage to the neck of the womb, failure to have proper intercourse or sexual disfunction. A whole range of disorders which may be related.

The patients who get to Hammersmith are the lucky ones. I can't treat half a million infertile couples. I can treat 6,000 a year, and *that* is a hell of a lot. We see 6,000 couples, and for IVF we treat about 700 per year. What is very sad about England is that while we have undoubtedly the best reproductive research in the world, and the Cambridge set-up has dominated world reproductive medicine so that this country is looked to from all over the world, including the United States, our clinical treatment of infertile people is abysmal. Only seven out of 200 health districts in England and Wales have really adequate infertility services.

One of the things that disturbs me is that every single university department in this country is toying with the idea of setting up its own test tube baby unit, or has already done so, because of peer pressure, because of the macho image that test tube baby treatment has, because the press has sung the praises of test tube baby treatment and that this is the treatment to conduct – the way of the future. And yet it is actually, of all infertility treatments, the most expensive, the most demanding, the most invasive and the least successful. And the paradox really is that there is no doubt in my mind that if a modest increase in investment for test tube baby programmes was actually put into developing routine infertility treatments, most couples would be much better off. Especially in the area of counselling, for example. We are very, very bad on counselling in this country. We are appalling at tubal surgery and we are bloody awful at hormonal treatments, to give you three really big areas. And all of those are a great deal cheaper than test tube baby treatments.

The embryo research we are doing I see as one of the most important developments in the whole of medical practice. What we are doing is to examine how embryos function in the first few days after fertilization, and I think that this will lead off in several major areas. Improvement in treatment of infertility, that there is no question of. But the single most important unsolved area facing human medicine in the 1990s is the problem of genetic disease. At least 10 per cent of human disease is genetic in origin, and probably another 10 per cent has a genetic component, such as heart disease, diabetes, cancer and so on. Now embryo research and the relationship to genetic biology enables us to start looking for the first time at gene defects. What we are really talking about is the ability to detect abnormal genetic structures in the human embryo and use the *in vitro* fertilization technology to prevent the birth of children that would die in childhood or who would be very severely deformed. And the future of this medicine holds the promise of gene therapy, so that people who have an inherent chance because of their genetic structure of developing cancer or diabetes or whatever, may possibly have very early gene therapy at the embryonic stage which will correct that tendency. And, of course, if that happens, and I believe it could happen within decades, that must be one of the most important areas of medical research.

The embryo is a hundredth of the size of a full stop on this page; it is invisible to the naked eye. What we are doing is removing a single cell from a structure that size. When I talk about an embryo, I am not talking about what the pro-LIFE people are talking about, which is really a foetus; I am not interested in the embryo after fourteen days, I am looking at the first two weeks after fertilization, the two weeks during which the menstrual period has not yet occurred.

And when you see these gory photographs of babies being aborted on the front page of the newspapers, one despairs of ever getting any rational argument.

You see, there is a great problem in this country at the moment. Should embryo research be banned? I think that it would be a disaster if it is. I have already painted the scenario which suggests that it is really quite a vital area of medicine. And there is another reason why I think it shouldn't be banned, and that is simply because the human embryo, certainly up to the fourteenth day, is not an individual, because up to the fourteenth day it can still twin. Secondly, only a small proportion of embryos which are formed in natural life *in utero* actually survive and become foetuses; most of them are shed with the menstrual fluid. And we are talking about a structure which . . . if I rub my hands together like that, I have just shed now into the air of this room 100 or 200 cells, all of which are bigger than the human embryo, all floating around, all with my genetic imprint which is unique to me. So the idea that the human embryo is unique is only a matter of qualification. Indeed, when a man ejaculates 200,000,000 sperm, each one of those sperm is genetically unique and equally alive, and yet nobody regards the sperm as being sacrosanct.

Take the child with Lesch–Nyhan syndrome, say, who will be born completely normal, but within a few months of birth will become very obviously mentally defective, who will have cerebral palsy and will get intractable pain, abdominal and chest pain, who will start to mutilate himself, bite his tongue and mouth off, throw himself downstairs, or whatever, and who will inevitably die of that disease within a few years of birth in cruel, demanding circumstances, all of which eventually destroys that family's unity.

And I give you Lesch–Nyhan as an example because that is the disease model that we are working on with our embryo research, because there is one particular gene defect which is very easy to recognize in the embryo, and we needed an easy gene defect to recognize first to get the work initiated. It's not a common disease, but it is typical of the many genetic diseases that we are trying to work to prevent.

Again and again, one of the accusations that I have from people is that we are taking on a godlike role and deciding who should live and who should die, who should have this treatment and who shouldn't. The patients themselves have to choose what they want to do. I'm not creating life. The idea that the test tube baby doctor is someone creating life in a test tube is not true. All he's simply doing is allowing life to be generated by providing the right milieu for it. And, potentially, in the future with the kind of embryo research we're doing, he will be able to prevent the worst kind of genetic defects. But that's hardly godlike; it's really just enhancing the quality of life, it's not altering it in any fundamental way. Creation is very different.

Even if you win a Nobel Prize, within about ten or fifteen years, the best you will hope to have is a tiny footnote in the bottom of some huge textbook which nobody will read anyway, because human progress goes on and people don't remember what you have done. But to leave behind your children, that is something which no matter how poor or disadvantaged you are, you do leave your own genetic background on this planet when you have finished with it and when it is finished with you. And I suppose that when I am gone, the most important thing will not be the work I have done, but Tanya, Joel and Benjamin. There is something very special about bringing on the next generation which infertile people are missing, and therefore there is something colossally constructive about this kind of work.

If you look at the fallopian tube under the microscope, the thing that strikes you is its colossal beauty. I mean, it is an incredibly beautiful structure. It is quite wondrous to look at: its colour – the tube is bright red because it is so thin and covered with a huge number of blood vessels – its texture, its complexity, the way it is designed and the huge puzzle of it. I mean, the fact is, even after all the work that we have done, we only understand a small part of its function. What that tube is doing at the time of ovulation is to actually actively transport sperm towards the ovary, and what is so remarkable is that while the sperm are being transported in this direction, the egg is being transported actively in the opposite direction. Here is a tube which is capable of transporting two gametes, egg and sperm, in totally different directions simultaneously so that they arrive at the same point, and then, having fertilized the egg, maintaining a controlled time course so that the fertilized egg arrives in the uterus ninety-six to 106 hours after fertilization. Now, that is so well programmed that if you take a fertilized egg from the outer end of the tube and put it in the inner end of the tube, it will immediately move back to where it was removed and continue its programmed descent into the uterus.

You have to stop and look occasionally. Sometimes when I am doing tubal surgery, you suddenly see the tube there in all its glory, and you have to look at it and wonder. Just the other day I flooded a pelvis with clear fluid so the tubes floated in that fluid, and everybody in the theatre stopped and stared, and someone said, 'My goodness, look at that, it is like a sea anemone.' I mean, that was a spontaneous reaction, it wasn't just me.

STEVE WRIGHT

NURSE

=====

I was brought up in Radcliffe, which is about five or six miles north of Manchester. Working-class background, council house, father was a mill worker, mother a housewife, what you would call a very traditional working-class upbringing, and the only significant difference was that I was considered bright enough to be sent to a grammar school. University was a possibility, but my parents wanted me to leave school and get a job.

Like a lot of people in the late sixties, I'd been wandering around Europe and growing my hair long, and I came back to face the reality of settling down and finding a job. I worked in a factory for a while, I worked in the tax office, things like that. And then a neighbour of mine who was a nurse suggested I might find nursing interesting. So I went to the local hospital for Radcliffe, which is in a town called Bury, just purely on an exploratory visit, and next thing I knew, I signed a form saying I would come and work there. The old matron showed me around, and we had a very nice, pleasant, chatty conversation. I didn't realize I was actually being interviewed, but looking back, of course, they were quite desperate to get recruits in those days. Literally, it was meant to be an informal visit, so I can't say I came into nursing with burning desires, but I quite liked the idea of working with people rather than things, and it just sort of fell in from there.

I'm now one of those people who have very strong reservations about the time at which we start to bring nurses into nursing. I'm not convinced that many people of eighteen or nineteen have developed psychological and social skills that enable you to cope with nursing, and that if they came into nursing a few years later they would find it easier because they would have more life experience. I mean, when I started, if patients were difficult and awkward with me, I tended to respond to the patient in like manner. You hadn't developed the maturity of outlook to recognize and understand why people behave in the way they do.

But I did genuinely enjoy it; I liked the sort of comradeship of being in a hospital, I liked the people I worked with. I was working with a bunch of nurses and untrained nursing auxiliaries with tremendous team spirit and good will, but they just didn't know what they were doing, they lacked guidance. A lot of the auxiliaries were mature, married women, working-class Bury people. Quite hard-working, essentially kind and caring, but I didn't like the way they were dealing with the patients. They were caring in the sense that they were well-meant, and they genuinely thought they were doing a good job, but at the time the nurses were quite aggressive with the patients who were aggressive with them, rather like you might be with someone in the pub, but not something you'd expect a nurse to be with a patient.

I was on an elderly ward, geriatric as it was then called, and it was packed with patients, and all the patients were kept in bed most of the time. There was about one or two feet between the beds, with the cot sides up to keep them in bed. The patients were terribly confused, they had sores, and nurses were essentially just coming on duty, washing, bathing and feeding them and going off again. It was very dispiriting, very dehumanizing. Patients weren't treated as individuals, they were treated like babies that had nothing in their heads at all.

It was my first experience of actually having very close and intimate contact with people in a caring sense. I don't think I'd seen that many people with no clothes on before, other than sort of mates at school in the showers, but actually seeing adults with no clothes on was quite an unusual thing for me, particularly older adults.

I think male nurses tend to be fairly ordinary folk, but I do think there are certain traits and qualities which equip you for being a good nurse. Often it's not something that you develop, more something that you are mature enough not to suppress. My belief is that any human being can care for another, but what our culture does is socialize those abilities out of people. For example, certainly in the culture I grew up in, the traditional man has to be big and strong, ride motorbikes, like football, drink a lot, bed as many women as you could, and go into tough, hard jobs. Now, for men who are nursing, they actually have to challenge the established norms about what men are and what women are. But I think it is easier now than it was when I started nursing nearly twenty years ago, because the sexual stereotypes are less strict.

Well, male nurses are all supposed to be gay, limp-wristed and camp. That is the stereotype image of the male nurse, which is actually quite untrue. You certainly get that with friends socially. I mean, all my mates fell about laughing and used to pull my leg something rotten when they heard I'd gone into nursing. You know, 'There must be something going wrong with him . . .' And even now you will still meet people who, if you say you're a nurse, look at you a bit funny. I mean, my kids' friends don't believe nurses can be men.

But you'll find male nurses who fit all the types, from the macho man down to the camp gay. And it doesn't mean they are any less manly because they do something which ostensibly seems rather feminine, which is caring. What actually makes me angry is the assumption by some people that if you are caring and kind and generally wish to help people that somehow there's something wrong with you, because those things are exclusively feminine. They are not. You know, the art and science of nursing is not exclusive to women; in fact, historically, men were the original nurses. In the earlier cultures that actually established some kind of caring profession, the carers were men. It happened in Egypt and it happened in India, and they were sort of part-priests, part-nurses, part-carers as it were – I mean, they weren't called nurses. The Knight's Hospitallers, for example, in the Middle Ages, they were all men; it wasn't considered to be a womanly thing to do, caring for somebody else. And only latterly did women as carers develop with nuns taking it on as part of their role.

I used to dread saying I was a nurse. Years ago, I admit I usually said, 'A *male* nurse', and I always put the 'male' on it. Now I don't. I just say, 'I'm a nurse', and if people flinch, that's their problem. I'm quite happy to explain my case, but I think by treating it in a matter of fact way, I help other people to get used to the idea. But you do still meet quite a lot of people who raise their eyebrows when you say you're a nurse.

Nursing is still seen as second in status to medicine by many doctors, but there are more and more doctors around now who are saying we are equal partners.

I think it's symbiotic. Nurses can't do what they do without doctors, and doctors can't do what they do without nurses. There are areas where at times doctoring is more significant than nursing, and there are areas where nursing is more significant than medicine. For example, medical input immediately prior to and during an operation is very, very high. You're dependent on the doctor's surgical skill and everything. But as soon as that is over with, the doctoring input gets less and less. After an operation, you might not actually need a doctor for months on end, but you depend more and more on nurses to help you with your basic living activities, like how to wash and dress and feed yourself and so on.

There's a tendency to rationalize our low pay by saying, 'Well, in the end my job is more important'. There is an element of martyrdom in nursing. I wonder how far that relates to the psyche of nurses in that there actually is a need to feel needed themselves. I don't think nurses often recognize it. I certainly do; I recognize that my big kick out of nursing is feeling that I am needed. I enjoy that. I know my job is valuable and it helps people.

But I think I deserve more money. Probably everybody says that. It niggles me sometimes when I look at jobs that other people I know of are in. I see people having to work less hard than I do, having less responsibility than I do, and yet earning a good deal more – and I resent the whizz kids in the City of London, making killings in stocks and shares. There are many nurses who deserve far more money for the quality of life they're giving.

But I do actually feel that for me the recompense is the pleasure, the interest and the stimulation that I get. The best part of the job undoubtedly is the immense kicks and sense of reward you can get from patients where you know they're better because something you've done has helped, has healed, has made them feel better. The feeling within yourself after many years in nursing that you're an expert, you know what you're talking about, you can articulate to patients and to doctors, and you feel confident and assured. That's great.

The worst part of it is the organization in which we have to work, which is still extremely bureaucratic, very slow and unresponsive to change. The sense that much of what you do is constrained by lack of resources, you know, seeing nurses working themselves down into the ground trying to do a good job simply because there aren't enough nurses around . . . there isn't enough money being put into health care, despite government figures that suggest the opposite – I don't think they're offering a true picture.

I tend to think a lot about nursing. I read a lot about nursing, I speak a lot about nursing, both in my own time and in my professional time and I write about it. And I think I'm the only consultant nurse in the country. Thameside was the first one to create the role.